KU-040-475

PROTECT
OUR
PLANET

THIS BOOK
BELONGS TO

Elizabeth
Mackenzie

PROTECT
—OUR—
PLANET

An anniversary view from
the World Wildlife Fund

PETER KING

Introduction by Sir Peter Scott CBE DSC

Contributions from Douglas Adams, Brian Clark,
Margaret Drabble, Elspeth Huxley, Dervla Murphy,
David Shepherd, Tom Stoppard, Gore Vidal and
William Waldegrave

Quiller Press

'The penalty of failure is global
disaster. Success through conservation
can improve the welfare and happiness
of millions of people.'

David Attenborough.

Cover: Picture of a lemur taken in Madagascar
by Alain le Garsmeur
Previous page: Lush vegetation on Isabela, one
of the Galapagos Islands
Overleaf: Siberian tiger

First published 1986 by Quiller Press
50 Albemarle Street, London W1X 4BD
Copyright 1986, © text other than acknowledged
contributions: Peter King; compilation © Quiller Press
and World Wildlife Fund
ISBN 0 907621 78 3

Design by Tim McPhee; design and
production in association with
Book Production Consultants, Cambridge
Typesetting by Cambridge Photosetting Services
Printed and bound in Yugoslavia
by Mladinska Knjiga

richard on?

Contents

Introduction by Sir Peter Scott

The World Wildlife Fund is an international conservation organisation with its headquarters in Switzerland, and 23 affiliate organisations throughout the world. WWF was established in 1961 by a small group (of which I am proud to have been one), as a channel through which popular concern for conservation could be directed into effective action. Since its foundation WWF has raised and spent over £60 million on more than 4,000 projects worldwide.

Twenty-five years after its formation, WWF faces a daunting task. That task involves a radical alteration of human attitudes and behaviour – the acceptance of collective and individual responsibility – in order to prevent the disappearance of the natural resources we take for granted. Through overpopulation, ignorance and indifference, mankind is exploiting the earth's natural resources and habitats – soil, air, forests, seas, rivers and wetlands – beyond the point of regeneration.

Statistics and predictions make frightening reading. One hundred and fifty years ago the world's human population was 1 billion. Today it is 4.75 billion. The population of India today is larger than that of the world in 1800.

The world's arable land area is currently calculated at 1.3 billion hectares. If the present rate of degradation continues it is estimated that 275 million hectares, or 20 per cent, will have been lost by the year 2000 – and the world's population will have increased by more than 20 per cent, to 6 billion.

Similarly, tropical rain forests, vitally important as the world's watersheds, home of the greatest diversity of plant and animal species on earth and containing many substances which are of use to man – in medicine for example – are being destroyed at the rate of 12 million hectares per year. If that rate of destruction continues there will be no forest left in 40 year's time.

It is all too easy to ignore statistics. WWF's task in the years immediately ahead is to make governments, institutions, industry and individuals listen and act. We cannot continue to squander and destroy the natural resources upon which all life depends. Conservation is not about 'good works' or philanthropy. It is about survival.

Mountain Lion

HRH the Duke of Edinburgh, the first President of the British World Wildlife Fund (now President of World Wildlife Fund International), with Peter Scott, later knighted for services to the cause of wildlife conservation.

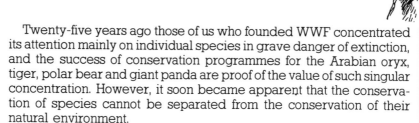

Twenty-five years ago those of us who founded WWF concentrated its attention mainly on individual species in grave danger of extinction, and the success of conservation programmes for the Arabian oryx, tiger, polar bear and giant panda are proof of the value of such singular concentration. However, it soon became apparent that the conservation of species cannot be separated from the conservation of their natural environment.

It is time for conservation and development interests to realise that they share common aims and that the dependence of every human being on the stability of the natural environment must unite us all.

Internationally, the world's wetlands – which are vitally important to man for fisheries, agriculture, grazing and water storage – have become one of the main targets for project action. Similarly, the world's oceans, coasts and islands – vital for the provision of foods, minerals, oil, natural gas and much of the air we breathe – need careful management and conservation and much more research.

Many countries, including for example Ethiopia, China and Thailand, want to co-operate with WWF in the preparation of conservation programmes and take action to prevent the degradation of their land, the pollution of their water and the careless destruction of their flora and fauna.

Few of us thought, 25 years ago, that conservation of the global environment would be so firmly established in the mainstream of human progress as it now is. I am sometimes asked which landmarks I personally recall as significant in WWF's history – and this shift of emphasis, from the particular to the general, from the endangered species to the global environment, which began in the 1970s, is certainly one of them.

A much earlier landmark for me came in the mid 1960s, when I realised how much young people, and particularly the young people in England, supported the aims of WWF. I recall that, after one of my television programmes at that time, I received a cascade of letters from school children indicating their willingness to help in saving the world's wildlife. This convinced me that conservation education was (and still is) the most important thing that any of us can do to save the earth from its most destructive animal species.

In terms of personal experience, I cannot ever forget the visit that my wife and I paid to the Panda Reserve at Wolong in China. The Chinese had told us they could not be sure of showing us a wild panda, but they could absolutely guarantee to show us fresh droppings. This they did, but although we never saw a wild panda, it was

'I cannot ever forget the visit that my wife and I paid to the Panda Reserve at Wolong in China.'

a fantastic experience to be in the thick bamboo forests high on the mountain slopes of Sichuan.

The panda is not only our symbol, it is I believe on the way to becoming one of our success stories. Another was the re-introduction of the Arabian oryx into Oman and Jordan. It gave me great satisfaction to see the first captive bred animals after their release in the Harassis desert in Oman. This wonderful animal was, as far as can be known, totally extinct in the wild for some ten years, and this is the *first* example of returning captive-bred animals to their original habitat after the extermination by man of the entire wild population of a species.

It is, of course, heartening to remember successes, but there is still so much to be done. Economic arguments are often put forward nowadays, as reasons to prove why we should be supporting conservation. I prefer to look at it as our duty as members of the human race, arguably the most 'highly' developed form of life on our planet, to pass on to posterity a natural world that is still worth living in.

Sir Peter Scott   9th April 1986

9

CHAPTER ONE

Defending Fur, Fin and Feather

One hundred years ago, fifteen middle-class ladies began to hold regular meetings in the country house of one of them, not far from London, calling themselves the Fur, Fin and Feather Folk. They were united by their passion for protecting wildlife, and they took the pledge never to wear the feathers of any bird not killed for food. About the same time, a group in Manchester formed a similar society, and eventually they joined forces, although, as the famous naturalist writer W. H. Hudson said, they were still just a few women against millions. Actually, by 1890, they numbered about 5000 but this was negligible in face of the forces against which they were fighting.

The conservationists did, however, have some powerful voices on their side, Queen Victoria's amongst them. In 1899 she confirmed an Army Order that officers should no longer wear egret plumes in their dress hats and 30 years before that she had written to her daughter in Germany, 'I wonder you could go to see the poor seals shot at! Papa could not bear their being shot, he was so fond of them!' Such feelings were rare in courtly circles, in which shooting was of course the most fashionable of occupations, and there would come a day when the most famous shot of the time would boast of bagging 19,135 birds and beasts in one year.

Slowly those men and women who believed in preserving life became better organised and they received helpful recognition (the Society for the Prevention of Cruelty to Animals had become Royal as early as 1840). Their researches into world-wide abuse became more sophisticated, and the realisa-tion took hold that there were broader issues to be addressed than fur, fin and feather. The conservationists were fighting not only against mindless cruelty, but against the deeply held belief that the human race had been given a 'passport to progress'. Indeed, most conservationists themselves, like the rest of us, firmly held the view that the knowledge and intelligence and perception of their societies could and would be readily transmitted to those parts of the world that were less 'developed'.

Twenty-five years ago the general view was that as the countries of Asia and Africa moved one by one, bloodily or peacefully, to independence, with self-government they would achieve prosperity, *development* would gradually abolish poverty and

HRH the Prince of the Netherlands, first President of WWF International, during his official visit to Ethiopia in 1969.

Forest destruction in Brazil.

malnutrition, and the Third World would progress to match the living standards of Western civilised societies. It has not happened. Many believe, perhaps correctly, that it was wrong to think that it would happen, at any rate in that way.

This is not a book about development – although it is essential to the story because the power behind the conservation movement was created, at least partly, by a disillusion with development. Some twenty-five years ago those who believed that it was right to conserve the world for future generations (just as great pictures were preserved for posterity) began to speak with more powerful voices as the mistakes of some development strategies became clearer. 'Man is the lord of creation, king of all he surveys,' wrote Elspeth Huxley in the early 1960s (see pp. 88–89), and 'A good lord does not destroy his fellow-creatures, nor a king reduce the world he surveys to a wasteland. . . . It will be a sad day – sad for man – if, looking through the window, he can see nothing but reflections of his own weary, baffled and disillusioned face.'

As the problems which development brought in its train became more obvious, in some cases more scandalous even, a reasoned criticism stood a better chance of being heard. No one could disagree, after all, with those who said that the deforestation of large tracts of the Amazon – with the loss and disturbance of human, animal and plant communities – had gone too far. There were far too many other examples. As a result, conservationists began to see that they would have to intervene in the world of action if the problems of development were to be overcome with sensitivity rather than violence, with understanding rather than conflict. This was the path taken by – amongst others – the World Wildlife Fund. The background is well summed-up by the distinguished Canadian conservationist Maurice Strong:

The very concept of conservation has itself changed to a significant degree in recent times. In the past, the emphasis was often on preservation, on resistance to development . . . Now the emphasis has shifted to a more positive and dynamic concept of the *care, stewardship and wise use of resources. . .*

The deforestation of large tracts of the Amazon and the disturbance of many human communities has gone too far.

Natural resources themselves are in a constant state of change, human interventions are a necessary part of that process and the primary role of the conservationist is to ensure that the process is managed in such a way as to prevent destruction of the resources and to maintain the integrity and the beauty of the ecosystems of which they are a part.

There is thus a direct and inevitable link between conservation – and human intervention . . . which we commonly refer to these days as development.

The next chapter explains how WWF came into being; the object of this chapter has been to place those beginnings into historical perspective – to explain that the conservation movement was already a powerful lobby by the early 1960s although perhaps it lacked cohesion. It certainly lacked financial support and sensitive direction, and that is what, at the appropriate time, WWF was able to supply.

This book continues by exposing the threat to the resources of our planet which will overtake us if we do not take positive action now. We live by those resources, and therefore our lives will be threatened. The problems of endangered species have been much publicised, and perhaps there are those who think that if a species of wildlife is lost, it is the equivalent of the sale and export of a Stubbs masterpiece from the United Kingdom to a museum in California. The painting has been 'lost' to the British nation. But has it? It can still be seen in its new home. The lost species of mammal will never be seen again. Plant species are also being lost at an alarming pace, undermining the ability of all animals – including man – to survive. Here is the comment of Grenville Lucas, the Curator of the

Herbarium, Royal Botanic Gardens, Kew, and Chairman of the Species Survival Commission of the International Union for Conservation of Nature:

At Kew we have a computer-based intelligence system which connects over 120 of the major botanic gardens of the world to produce a steady stream of lists of plants, in order to ensure a full propagation programme for all the rarer species. There is, though, always a temptation sitting in an office with all this data flowing into the computer to think how successful we are. But it is only when we recommend action that we begin the work of conservation – and only when that action is actually taken, that we achieve something. Actually I believe that we could still face a total disaster in our attempts to save the plant life of our planet – a disaster which would make the desertification of the Sahel region look like a minor affair. However much relief is provided by the botanic gardens; it is in their habitats in the real world that the war will be won. We have still a long way to go, and given determination and the necessary funding, it can be done.

The endangered plant 'dove's beak' (right) is one of thousands of threatened animal and plant species held in a vital data bank at the Conservation Monitoring Centre in Cambridge.

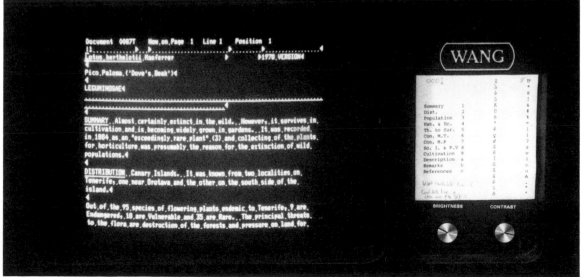

Gore Vidal in the Gobi Desert

On a high hill with dark mountains behind, the Gobi stretches as far as anyone could wish, the flatness broken by the odd mountain, set island-like in the surrounding gravel. I got out of the jeep to commune with the silence. The driver started to pluck at small dark green clumps of what turned out to be chives. We ate chives and looked at the view and I proceeded to exercise the historical imagination and conjured up Genghis Khan on that famous day when he set his standard of nine yak-tails high atop Gupta, and the Golden Horde begain its conquest of Europe.

We stopped at an oasis – a bright strip of ragged green in the dark shining gravel. Water bubbles up from the earth and makes a deep narrow stream down a low hill to a fenced-in place where a Mongol grows vegetables for the camp. The water is cool and pure and the Mongols with us stare at it for a time and smile; then they lie down on their bellies and drink deeply. We all do. In fact, it is hard to get enough water in Gobi. Is this psychological or physiological? The Mongol gardener showed me his plantation. 'The melons don't grow very large,' he apologised, holding up a golfball of a melon. 'It is Gobi, you see.' I tried to explain to him that if he were to weed his patch, the vegetables would grow larger, but in that lunar landscape I suspect that the weeds are as much a delight to him as the melons.

We were told that close to camp there is a famous watering hole, where, at sundown, the snow leopard lies down, as it were, with the wild ass. But we had missed sundown. Nevertheless, ever-game, our party walked half-way to the hole before settling among rocks on a ridge to fortify ourselves with alien spirits against the black desert night that had fallen with a crash about us. As we drank, we were joined by a large friendly goat.

We checked out the watering hole, which turned out to be a muddy place in the rocks; there were no signs of beasts. Again, we were on the move; this time south-easterly toward the Mount Mother system. The heat was intense. We glimpsed a wild ass, wildly running up ahead of us. Some gazelles skittered in the distance. The countryside was almost always horizontal but never pleasingly flat. To drive over such terrain is like riding a Wild West bronco. As we penetrated deeper into the preserve, vegetation ceased. What thornwood there was no longer contained greenery. Thornwood – with camel and goat dung – provides the nomads with their fuel. We were told that

14

Captive-bred Przewalski horses are to be returned to the Great Gobi National Park.

poachers are more apt to steal the wood in the preserve than the animals.

Suddenly, all of our jeeps converged on the same spot, close to the steep dark red Khatan Khairkhan, an island of rock rising from a dry sea. The Mongol drivers gathered around a circle of white sand some six feet in diameter. Three spurts of icy water bubbled at the circle's centre. Again, the happy smiles. Mongols stare at water rather the way northerners stare at fires. Then each of us tried the water. It tasted like Badoit. Camel and wild-ass dung in the immediate vicinity testified to its excellent, even curative, mineral qualities.

Half-way up the red mountain, we made camp at the mouth of a ravine lined with huge smooth red rocks – glacial? – remains of a sea that had long since gone away? No geologist was at hand to tell us but in the heights above the ravine there were the Seven Cauldrons of Khatan Khairkhan where, amongst saxaul groves and elm trees, the waters have made seven rock basins.

Even rarer than a functioning lamasery in Mongolia is the Przewalski horse. They exist in zoos around the world but whether or not they are still to be found in Gobi is a subject of much discussion. Some think that there are a few in the Chinese part of the Gobi; some think that they are extinct. In any case, the Great Gobi National Park plans to reintroduce – from the zoos – the Przewalski horse to its original habitat. We drank to the Przewalski horse. We drank to the plane that was to pick us up the next morning when we returned to base. 'Would it really be there?' I asked. 'No problem.'

CHAPTER TWO

How It All Started

Two British newspapers played a crucial role in the successful launching of the World Wildlife Fund twenty-five years ago. One was the *Observer*, which early in 1960 published an article by the eminent zoologist Sir Julian Huxley; the other was the *Daily Mirror*, which gave the new organisation a basis for its financial security by publicising its proposals. What happened was this. One Sunday towards the end of 1960, the *Observer* article in which Sir Julian described what he had found in Africa was read by a Mr Victor Stolan, a German who had become a naturalised Briton, and was living in London. The following day, 6 December, Mr Stolan's first action on arriving at his office was to dictate a letter to Sir Julian, care of the *Observer*. It read:

'It was with admiration and anxiety that I read your articles in the *Observer*. Only reluctantly, I add mine to the large number of letters which you must have received in response to your outstanding and astounding survey.

But alas, however excellent your suggestions to remove the danger threatening the African wildlife, I feel that without a vigorous and immediate action to raise the great funds needed the irreparable detriment will not be prevented from becoming a fact.

There must be a way to the conscience and the heart and pride and vanity of the very rich people to persuade them to sink their hands deeply into their pockets and thus serve a cause which is greater and nobler than any other one.

A single and uninhibited mind must take charge of such a world-embracing situation. I hasten to add that I am not such a person. However, I have some ideas as to how to collect substantial donations but nobody of sufficient importance to speak to. Would you care to put me in touch with somebody with whom such ideas can be developed and speedily directed towards accumulating some millions of pounds without mobilising commissions, committees, etc., as there is no time for Victorian procedure.

Since my naturalisation, I am proud to call this country mine, but I cannot help feeling that it has become a country of understatements, of gentle talk with not enough push behind it.

If, on the other hand, what is left of wildlife in Africa (and elsewhere for that matter) is to be saved, a blunt and ruthless demand must be made to those who, with their riches, can build for themselves a shining monument in history. . .'

When he received the letter, Sir Julian decided to pass it on to a friend, Max Nicholson, Director-General of the British Nature Conservancy (now the Nature Conservancy Council), a body responsible for advising the British Government on all issues relating to wildlife and natural habitats. Nicholson knew that Peter Scott, the well-known ornithologist, was in sympathy with the idea that there should be a large-scale international effort to raise really substantial sums of money for conservation. Scott, a man of many interests, was at the time a Vice-President of the International Union for Conservation of Nature (IUCN) and Scott and Nicholson discussed Stolan's letter which put into words an idea which had been floating around for several months.

Early the following year there happened to be two meetings at which Nicholson was able to discuss further the ideas set out by Stolan. The first was in the United States in March, and at the second, a conference in York, England, of the British Ornithologists' Union. Nicholson talked to a prominent member, Guy Mountfort. The latter, when he was not watching birds, was head of a large advertising agency, and so was able to offer advice about the promotional and business aspects of Stolan's scheme. He was enthusiastic about the prospects for success.

Over the Easter holiday, then, these three men – Scott, Nicholson and Mountfort – got together a paper which set forth the outline of the scheme. All three knew of the activities of IUCN. Founded twelve years earlier, the International Union for Conservation of Nature, which had headquarters in Switzerland, was an independent organisation with an expert staff funded by states, government agencies, and other major national and international non-governmental conservation agencies. There was already a feeling within IUCN that their activities were severely hampered by lack of money. It was widely said that what they needed was 'an International Red Cross for Wildlife'. So the three men arranged for their paper to be discussed at a meeting of the Executive Board of IUCN at its headquarters at Morges late in April. To their satisfaction, the Board approved the proposal in principle.

Julian Huxley and Max Nicholson travelled together in Spain in 1957 and discussed the urgent need for funding the conservation movement.

To repeat, the proposal was to form a *professional* organisation to raise the money needed to put the worldwide conservation movement on a proper footing. In the way that these things happen, various like-minded people got together to support the idea, and it was decided to form a group to hold a meeting. This took place in London in May 1961.

Thus, only a few months after Mr Stolan's letter, the first efforts to put his ideas into action were in train.

The aim of those meetings was to examine the requirements and prepare the plans for the establishment of the world-wide fund-raising organisation. This would work in collaboration with existing bodies to bring massive financial support to the conservation movement. They also had to find a name for the body they were founding, and discussed various ideas.

Finally, everyone settled on the full name *World Wildlife Fund.* They all agreed that the newly established WWF should have a President and, after the meeting, Prince Bernhard of the Netherlands accepted the invitation to serve. Later HRH the Duke of Edinburgh expressed interest and agreed to become President of its British National Appeal. The need for a logo was also discussed, and Gerald Watterson, Director-General of IUCN, produced a doodle of a giant panda which Peter Scott took away and turned into the professional logo we know today. The advantage of the panda as logo was that the animal was one of the best-loved in the world – and it also reproduced clearly in black and white print.

The next priority was to seek funds. Two members of the group put up a total of £3000 (the equivalent of £20,000 in 1986) to prime the pump. Subsequently, Mr Jack Cotton, a well-known British businessman (now dead), donated a further £10,000. With this basic funding available, it would be possible to mount a campaign, the philosophical basis of which was a document known as the Morges Manifesto (after the village of the same name in the Canton of Vaud, Switzerland, where WWF had its first international headquarters). It read as shown overleaf.

It was signed by sixteen of the world's leading

THE MORGES MANIFESTO

All over the world to-day vast numbers of fine and harmless wild creatures are losing their lives or their homes as the result of thoughtless and needless destruction. In the name of advancing civilisation they are being shot or trapped out of existence on land taken to be exploited, or drowned by new dams, poisoned by toxic chemicals, killed by poachers for gain, or destroyed in the course of political upheaval.

In this senseless human activity the 1960s promise to beat all past records for wiping out the world's wildlife.

Doubtless, feelings of guilt and shame will follow and will haunt our children, deprived of nature's rich inheritance by ignorance, greed and folly. But although the eleventh hour has struck it is not yet quite too late to think again. Skilful and devoted men, and admirable organisations, are struggling to save the world's wildlife. They have the ability and the will to do it, but they tragically lack the support and resources. They are battling at this moment on many fronts and against many daily changing and growing threats. They need above all money to carry out mercy missions and to meet conservation emergencies by acquiring land where wildlife treasures are threatened, and in many other ways. Money, for example, to pay guardians of wildlife refugees, money for education and propaganda among those who would care and help if only they understood; money to send out experts to danger spots and to train more local wardens and helpers, in Africa and elsewhere.

The emergency must be tackled with vigour and efficiency on the much enlarged scale which it demands, but success will depend not only on the devoted efforts of enthusiasts for wildlife, but on winning the respect and backing of many other interests which must not be overlooked or antagonised.

Mankind's self-respect and mankind's inheritance on this earth will not be preserved by narrow or short-sighted means!

Guy Mountfort with a Sindhi chief during his expedition to Pakistan.

conservationists: Professor Jean G. Baer (Switzerland), Dr C. J. Bernard (Switzerland), Professor François Bourlière (France), Wolfgang E. Burhenne (Germany), Dr Eugen Gerstenmaier (Germany), Charles Vander Elst (Belgium), Professor W. Goetel (Poland), Dr Edward H. Graham (USA), Sir Julian Huxley, FRS (UK), Rocco Knobel (South Africa), Dr Kai Curry-Lindahl (Sweden), E. M. Nicholson (UK), Erico C. Nicola (Switzerland), S. K. Shawki (Sudan), Peter Scott (UK), Dr E. B. Worthington (UK).

Then, on 11 September 1961, less than ten months after the original Stolan letter, WWF was legally constituted under Swiss law at Zurich, registered as a tax-exempt charitable foundation.

It was now time to announce the news to the world. A public meeting was held on 26 September 1961 at the Royal Society of Arts in London. The main address was given by Sir Julian Huxley, supported by Professor Bowers, President of IUCN, and by Peter Scott. The latter was soon to be elected first Vice-President and Chairman of WWF. A Charter for the organisation was announced.

One object of all this had been to obtain publicity, and publicity there was. But the most amazing coup was still to come. A well-known public relations consultant, Ian MacPhail, had joined WWF in July, and in September, shortly after the RSA meeting, he had lunch with the Chief Executive of the *Daily Mirror* group of newspapers, Sir Hugh Cudlipp, and told him that he had a first-class 'story' but that it must receive first-class treatment if the *Mirror* was to be given it as an exclusive feature. Cudlipp, rather surprisingly, agreed. The following Saturday, 7 October, a car fetched MacPhail from his home and drove him to the newspaper's editorial offices. He was told by the assembled journalists that Monday's edition would be what they called a SHOCK ISSUE, in which several news pages would be given over to this one topic. MacPhail asked for, and was given, page 1, page 3, the centre spread, and the back page. For the next two days he sat, literally, in the editor's chair, planning the pictures and the text to support the case of WWF, that 'a world crusade to beat the 20th century death flood' needed 'your support'. There was a coupon on the back page so that readers did not have to write a

WWF's first headquarters in Switzerland were in a converted country house.

letter in support – they only had to cut out the coupon and send it to the *Mirror* with a donation. The result was beyond all expectations. Readers immediately sent in sums ranging from a few pence to hundreds of pounds, and totalling in all £45,000, a huge amount, equivalent to £300,000 in 1986. It took MacPhail and his friends several days and nights to sort out the mail bags of letters which poured into the *Mirror* office. Thus this one article had put the WWF on a sound financial basis and the way ahead was clear.

Since then WWF has channelled funds to over 4000 projects in 130 countries which have given countless animals, plants and natural areas all over the world a better chance of survival.

How it works is this. The professional staff of IUCN has the expert advice of over 500 member organisations in 114 countries; its membership includes 56 states, 123 government agencies, and virtually all major national and international non-governmental conservation organisations. As a consequence, IUCN is uniquely qualified not only to advise WWF on priority projects but also to help supervise their implementation, and assess the results with WWF.

The major functions of IUCN staff are monitoring biological data and the status of resources which require conservation, developing plans for dealing with the problems which face conservationists, and supporting action arising from these plans by governments or other appropriate organisations.

These pages in the Daily Mirror *produced a huge response from readers, filling several bags of mail.*

CHAPTER THREE

Why We Save Wildlife

A tiger fitted with a miniature radio transmitter moves stealthily through the trees in India's forests. The tranquilliser which was used to put it to sleep so that the radio could be fitted, and the transistorised radio itself, were both funded by WWF. So was the small dam which ensures that there will be a water supply in the area where the tiger is going to drink. The object of the exercise is to gather information essential to the tiger's survival. And WWF also funded the radio equipment which the area's wardens will use to track down the poachers who are following the tiger.

Was this what the founders of WWF anticipated would happen to the funds they collected in those early days? Perhaps not. And is all the paraphernalia of modern science actually needed just to save a few hundred tigers? The answer to that question is that the tiger is an index of the quality of the human environment. To save the tiger, you must maintain the forest, and you must ensure there are spotted deer or other prey for it to eat. To preserve the deer, you must preserve vegetation, and that means you must preserve the soil; water conservation is an important factor too. So, in the name of the tiger, a total environmental conservation programme takes place, and that calls for a scientific approach and technical equipment.

The tiger stands at the apex of the animal kingdom – still the main attraction in zoos. It is the name selected for a warship or a baseball team as a symbol of excellence; a petrol company adopts the tiger for an advertising campaign which implies that its product supplies power. It was this status symbolism which inspired the public to suport the WWF programmes to save the tiger from extinction.

The *Operation Tiger* campaign in India has been running now for more than ten years, with the overall objective of ensuring that a viable population of tigers lives in the natural environment of the country. It started with eight reserves, and more have been added year by year. The programme is supported, in terms of both policy and funds, by the Indian Government. Its approach has been based on improving the ecosystem (see p. 60), with not only the tiger, but also the people of India, as the ultimate beneficiaries. The reserves cover over

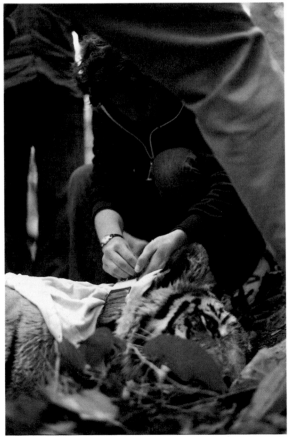

Putting a radio collar on a tiger in the Royal Chitiran National Park, Nepal.

The tiger stands at the apex of the animal kingdom.

10,000 square miles, and within the whole area all wildlife – mammals, birds, reptiles, rare flowers and butterflies – are thriving. Vegetation cover has revived, and water supplies, once threatened, are now good.

A parallel example is the Chinese giant panda, the well-known symbol of WWF itself, and there was a decade between the two campaigns. There are probably about a thousand pandas in China and in the reserves of the Sichuan Province, as shown in table overleaf.

They began to die of starvation when the bamboo itself, on which they depended for their diet, bloomed (see below) and died off. If the bamboo dies, so does the panda. But there were still many unanswered questions concerning the panda's diet. So a team of WWF-appointed scientists, headed by Dr George Schaller of the New York Zoological Society, entered Wolong, China, in late 1980 to work with top Chinese scientists to study the panda's

Big game hunting was a major pastime during the days of the Raj. This picture is taken from an advertisement for a 12-bore gun and carried the caption 'I have killed everything from tiger to snipe'.

requirements for survival in the wild. Their first step was to fit six wild pandas with radio-collars and ear-tags so that their movements could be followed.

Several questions puzzled the scientists. For example, although the panda appears to depend on the bamboo, it does not, like the cow, retain the fibrous content (which has very little nutritional value) for long in its digestive system. And the pandas do not even favour the most nutritious part of the bamboo anyway. Why? The answers to these questions would throw light on another crucial one – how much space does the panda need to survive? When is he crowded by human beings, what would the effect of overcrowding be on his social organization? These researches were not concerned with pandas alone. For example, it is known that predators, such as the bamboo rats, and insects, destroy a significant proportion of the bamboo plants in some areas, with the result that either the

Opposite: A unique picture of the giant panda in the wild in China.

There are probably less than a thousand pandas in China.

SURVEY OF PANDA RESERVES (APRIL TO JUNE 1983)

Name of Reserve	Size/ sq km	Estimated Number of Pandas
Jiuzhaigou	600	40
Wanglang	277	10–20
Tangjiahe	424	100–140
Fengtongzai	400	50
Dafending	300	30–40

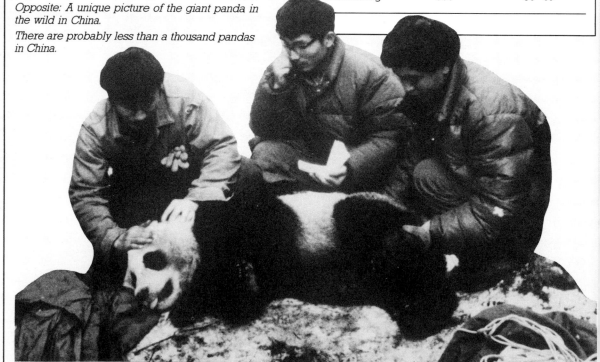

to help the animal through the difficult years ahead. Although one of the most difficult yet most important tasks in any study of an endangered species is to ascertain how many animals are left alive in the world, the evidence suggests that panda numbers continue to decline.

WWF has supported the establishment of species and habitat research for the ten reserves in China and pledged over $1 million of the $3 million needed by the Government to establish a centre of research in one of them.

It is not only animals such as the tiger and panda that are endangered. There are also the birds, the fish and other groups. An example is the giant Philippines eagle, which glides through the thick forests hunting monkeys, squirrels and flying lemurs. WWF has been funding activities to try to save this bird from extinction for some fifteen years now. The problem is – once again – the activities of man, primarily the development of the forest areas in which the eagle lives. Logging operations, for example, leave the eagle without anywhere to nest. The research teams also believe that despite the fact that large tracts of virgin forest are left intact, their structure may not be suitable for eagles. One solution therefore is to bring the eagles captive into breeding sites in hope that this will ensure the survival of the species. It is too early to say whether this will be successful.

Amphibians and reptiles are descendants of the earliest forms of vertebrate animals able to survive on land, and many of their species have provided man with sources of staple food and other products throughout his history. Yet by hunting in the feeding, breeding and nesting areas, man has put these creatures at risk. *Man Devolupus* is – yet again – to blame. He has an insatiable appetite it seems for turtle soup, tortoise-shell brushes and boxes, crocodile-leather wallets and handbags, to mention only a few luxury items. To meet his requirements, the crocodiles and the turtles are put in great danger and WWF has given them the highest priority in protection programmes.

Right: The giant Philippines eagle is one of the world's most endangered birds.

panda is starved of food, or he consumes too many of the available shoots, reducing the plant's chances of survival.

The bamboo is thus important for the pandas – but also for the people of the areas because it helps prevent erosion. The strange characteristic of bamboo is that it may reproduce regularly each year for about sixty years, and then suddenly – instead – flower, seed and die. Such a dying off tends to be synchronised, affecting all bamboo of the same species over a wide area of China. Recently up to 90 per cent of the bamboo in one region, round Wolong, died. And, to make matters worse, in their attempt to improve agricultural production, farmers in the area had eliminated alternative species, so search as hard as they might up and down the hillsides and valleys, the pandas could find no alternative diet. It may take ten years for stricken areas to regenerate.

In fact, about a quarter of the pandas left in the wild will face this kind of crisis at some time or other. In addition to the WWF team, China's Ministry of Forestry has prepared an emergency programme

Douglas Adams Follows the Lemur in Madagascar

Virtually everything that lives on Madagascar doesn't exist anywhere else on earth. It's as if this great island were a chunk of a different planet mysteriously embedded in the Indian Ocean. In fact it is more like a life-raft from a different age.

Among the wild variety of strange birds, chameleons, plants like triffids, tenrecs (a thing resembling a hedgehog), scarlet frogs and fruit bats, the eeriest creatures on this ancient life-raft are the lemurs – for they, like us, are primates. Millions of years ago these creatures lost their niche on the mainland to newcomers in the forests, the big-brained monkeys, who luckily arrived too late to reach Madagascar, which was already disappearing over the horizon. The monkeys, for the time being, had to make do with the rest of the world.

The aye-aye is a lemur, but such a peculiar one that it long went unrecognised as such. It is a solitary nocturnal creature. It looks a bit like a cat and a bit like a fox. It also has large bat's ears, a dog's snout and pointy little rabbit's teeth.

'Aye, aye' is supposed to be the cry of fear the Malagasi utter if they see one. Hardly anyone ever does. The creature is now pathetically rare and is poised on the edge of extinction. Ironically, considering the history of Madagascar as an island refuge, the aye-aye now has its own refuge away from the mainland – a deserted rain-forest island called Nosy Mangabé, which sits in a sheltered bay to the north-east of Madagascar. Nine aye-ayes were released there in 1966. Until recently it was feared that none of them had survived.

We explored the rain forest by the afternoon light. The richness of it is continually astonishing – an awe-inspiring complexity of inter-dependences of plant, animal and insect. It is all woven into the most meagre slippery soil, for the nutrients which feed and sustain the forest are stored above ground, in the bewildering array of trees. Cut down the trees, the red soil quickly washes away and you are left with nothing. The tragedy of Madagascar is that everybody knows this – and yet the people are so poor that they can only survive from day to day by plundering the forest.

That degree of poverty hardly allows for long-term planning, and the forest reserves are dwindling away at a terrifying rate. The last refuge of a hundred million years of unique life is disappearing.

The intriguing aye aye (opposite) is now pathetically rare.

Dervla Murphy Searches for the Sifaka in Madagascar

I was searching for Sifaka with their thick, silky, pure white coats. They needed no protective colouring before Man came to Madagascar. When feeding, resting or grooming they keep their long furry tails tucked between their hind legs, tightly curled. But as they leap – covering enormous distances with arms outstretched towards their branch-goal, as in a gesture of welcome – those tails plume out like horizontal parachutes.

During the early afternoon branches began to move in Lemurville: slight movements up and down the forested precipice. Would tea-time involve no more than sitting around invisibly (from our point of view) chewing berries and leaves? But soon the whole group, including a baby clinging to its mother's chest, bounded down into the main canyon where their forest overflowed on to the lower part of the yellow-grey wall. We rushed along our fissured cliff-top, disregarding the various injuries inflicted on us en route by the environment, and about a mile upstream found an ideal vantage-point from which to observe the sifakas' main area of operations until their sunset bedtime.

There could be no question of erecting our tent, but we used it as an anti-insect sleeping-bag, arranging the mosquito netting over our faces to allow for star gazing and ventilation. The least unsuitable 'bed' – a rock slab clear of vegetation – sloped radically and had numerous limestone protuberances.

Soon 3 of our sifaka were again visible, just below their cliff-top. I focused on them with affection; in that arid world of warped stone and hostile plants, of utter silence and immobility, those cheerful lively little creatures, in their lush inaccessible oasis, by now seemed close friends. It was good that they slept and played and fed and sun-worshipped beyond the reach of Man, as their ancestors had done for countless millennia before Man existed.

CHAPTER FOUR

It Tolls for Thee

When the Genoese Christopher Colombus was hired by the Spanish to find a western route to Jerusalem, he accidentally made 'The Discoveries', thus opening up the New World to both trade and religion. One of his least-known discoveries was that wonder of nature, the tropical rain forest. On seeing one area for the first time on 28 October 1492, Colombus wrote 'I never beheld so fair a thing; trees beautiful and green and different from ours, with flowers and fruits each according to their kind, many and little birds which sing very sweetly.' Dr John Donne, over a hundred years later, told us not to send to ask for whom the bell tolled – so we need not ask who will be the loser when a tropical forest is lost. Each of us, whether we live in a city or close to nature, is affected by the loss of tropical forest, by the decimation of plant species and by the disappearance of wetlands. We, as members of the human race, are not only affected by this deterioration, – we are the cause of it. Something like one in six of all the plants and micro-organisms in the world is being eliminated as the direct consequence of human action. This is taking place primarily in the tropics; yet if we do not live in the tropics ourselves, how, we might ask, can we be the cause of it – unless the word 'we' is used in a rather absurdly broad sense for *all* members of the human race?

As we read these words, it is frightening to know that of the 380,000 plant species known to man, some 40,000 species will disappear during our lifetime. So this is not a threat facing nameless, future generations, it is facing *us*. And to answer the question 'How are those of us who live in temperate zones responsible for the wholesale destruction in the tropics?', it is only necessary to look at what is being done in the name of 'development' – logging to provide the industrialised world with timber for housing, pulp for paper products, to give one example. The international trade in wood products earns nearly $6 billion for tropical countries, as well as providing employment, but at a vast cost to the environment. Clearance for crops, the rearing of livestock, and human settlement, all contribute to the destruction of forests.

Let us frighten ourselves with another statistic. By the time we have finished reading this page, somewhere in the world another 22 hectares of tropical moist forest will have been destroyed. Many tropical countries will lose virtually all their forest cover in the next twenty years if destruction continues at the present rate. Some have totally disappeared already.

Does it matter? Tropical forests are the world's greatest storehouses of biological diversity, containing nearly half the earth's total of plant and animal species. These species are of great benefit to members of the human race – forming the active ingredient of many of the drugs which are prescribed to cure our illnesses. Actually the potential value of plant life in the tropical forests has hardly been tapped, as the great majority of forest plants have not yet been analysed for useful compounds. Nevertheless, we go on destroying them, despite their potential benefit to us.

It is not only the prescription users of Western society who gain from the plant life of the tropics.

> A typical patch of rain forest, just four miles square, contains as many as 1500 species of flowering plants, up to 750 species of tree, 400 species of bird, 150 kinds of butterfly, 100 different types of reptile and 60 species of amphibian. The numbers of insects are so great that no one has been able to count them . . . but there may be as many as 42,000 species in these 2½ acres.
> *US National Academy of Sciences*

Right: Rafflesia arnoldii *is the largest flower in the world, found in the tropical rain forests in Indonesia.*

SOME WWF/IUCN CONSERVATION PROJECTS

Project No	Project Title
1955	Kenya, Training of Wildlife Department Field Rangers
1958	Mexico, Monarch Butterfly
1960	Indonesia, Ujung Kulon—Rhinoceros
1963	Indonesia, Ujung Kulon—Vegetation Survey
1964	Ghana, Elephant Conservation
1969	Uganda, Effects of Tree-felling on Rainforest Primates
1972	Malaysia, Sumatran Rhinoceros
1973	Dominica, Cabrits National Park
1974	Guatemala, Land Use and Natural Resources Survey
1976	Costa Rica, National Park Foundation
1982	Impact of Oil Pollution on Living Resources of Aquatic Environments
1987	Sri Lanka, Conservation Education
1994	WWF/IUCN Species Conservation Data Base
1988	The World Conservation Strategy and the European Community
2001	Integrating Conservation and Development Planning
2005	Promotion of a Network of Effectively Managed Terrestrial and Marine Protected Areas
2009	Developing and Evaluating the International Conservation Programme
3001	Thailand, Elephant
3009	Africa, Fuelwood in the Sahel
3010	Seychelles, Magpie Robin
3014	Wildlife Trade Monitoring Unit
3022	Kenya, Anti-poaching Unit
3023	Mauritius, Education Booklets for Children
3027	China, Giant Panda, Tangjiahe
3028	Trade in Rhino Products
3030	India, Elephant, Bihar and Orissa
3032	India, Elephant in South India
3035	Spain and Portugal, Conservation of Wolf
3039	Sierra Leone, Elephant
3044	Follow-up to World Conservation Strategy
3045	India, Turtles
3046	Ecuador, Galapagos Islands, Dark-rumped Petrel
3050	Malaysia, Wildlife Conservation Coordinator
3055	Madagascar, Tropical Rainforest Conservation
3059	Peru, Tropical Rainforest Conservation
3062	Mali, Niger River Delta
3064	Bahamas, Cat Island Turtle
3065	Antilles, Netherlands, Underwater Park Curaçao

Project No	Project Title
3069	Caribbean, Marine Resources Management
3072	WWF Co-Sponsorship of World National Parks Congress
3073	Resource Book on World Conservation Strategy
3074	China, International Whaling Commission Mission to Peking
3075	St. Lucia, Conservation, Maria Islands
3076	Costa Rica, La Amistad National Park
3077	Przewalski Horse Semi-Reserves
3078	Spain, Survey of Beach Photographers Misuse of Chimps
3082	Ethiopa, Mobile Unit for Conservation Education
3084	Europe, *Maculinea* Butterfly Sites
3085	Costa Rica, Sea Turtles
3087	Sri Lanka, Wildlife Conservation
3088	Indonesia, Warty Pig
3089	Educational Support Services for Developing Communities
3092	Greenland, Humpback Whale
3095	Training and Resource Centre for Developing Countries
3096	Guinea-Bissau, Conservation of Wetlands
3097	Ecuador, Evaluation of WWF/IUCN Project Activities in Galapagos
3101	Gambia, Chimpanzee Rehabilitation
3103	Sri Lanka, Mahaweli Basin Protected Areas
3105	Finland, Wild Forest Reindeer
3107	Meeting of SSC Elephant/Rhino Specialist Group
3108	Indonesia, Marine Conservation
3109	Mexico, Bolson Tortoise
3111	Uganda, Training Unit for Game Guards
3112	Nepal, Conservation Education
3116	Argentina, Hooded Grebe
3125	Workshop on Migratory Birds in Western Hemisphere
3127	Malaysia, Sabah—Crocodiles
3131	Brazil, Fishes in Amazonian Tributaries
3133	Indonesia, Sumatra—Conservation of Large Mammals and their Habitats
3134	Indonesia, Environmental Education and Training
3137	Caribbean, Coral Reef Management
3138	Zaire, Pygmy Chimpanzee
3139	Rumania, Fisheries and Pelicans in Danube Delta
3145	Pacific Islands, Marianas Bat
3146	Wetlands for the Neotropical Region
3147	Plant Campaign—Survey of Activities of International Organizations
3149	Mauritius, Plant Conservation

Project No	Project Title
3152	Caribbean, Natural Area Management
3157	Peru, Yellow-tailed Woolly Monkey
3206	Cameroon, Management Plan
3207	Ivory Coast, Tai National Park
3215	Brazil, Reintroduction of Gold Lion Tamarin
3216	Liberia, Sapo National Park
3234	*In situ* Gene Banks for Maintenance of Wild Genetic Resources in Tropical Forest Countries
3226	Brazil, Reserves for Endangered Bird Species

UK PROJECTS

Project No	Project Title
26/82	Holme Marsh (Norfolk Ornithological Association)
60/82	North Cliffe Woods (Yorkshire Naturalists Trust)
71/82	Magor Marshland Reserve (Gwent Trust for Nature Conservation)
106/83	Badger Working Group Report (CoEnCo)
99/83	Coastal Site Directory (Marine Conservation Society)
113/83	Conservation Officer (London Wildlife Trust)
120/83	Breney Common (Cornwall Trust for Nature Conservation)
37/84	Rutland Water Visitor Centre (Leics and Rutland TNC)
64/84	King's Wood Glebe Meadows (Bedfordsire County Council)
66/84	Dungeness (RSPB)
82/84	Endemic Flora of St Helena
111/84	Orchid Study (University of Sussex)
114/84	Moorland at Evie (RSPB)
118/84	Management, Chew Valley Lake (Bristol Waterworks Co)
119/84	Cheddar Woods (Somerset Trust for Nature Conservation)
126/84	The Scalp (Lincs and South Humberside Trust)
128/84	Long Clough (Derbyshire Naturalists' Trust)
147/84	Upland Breeding Birds (P Haworth)
148/84	Scar and Castlebeck Woods (The Woodland Trust)
150/84	Survey of Trade in Cacti & other Succulents (IUCN Cambridge)
154/84	Ouse Washes (The Wildfowl Trust)
168/84	Liaison Officer (Wildlife Link Badger Group)
1/85	Ballachuan Hazel Wood (Scottish Wildlife Trust)
6/85	Skipwith Common Grazing Project (Yorkshire Wildlife Trust)

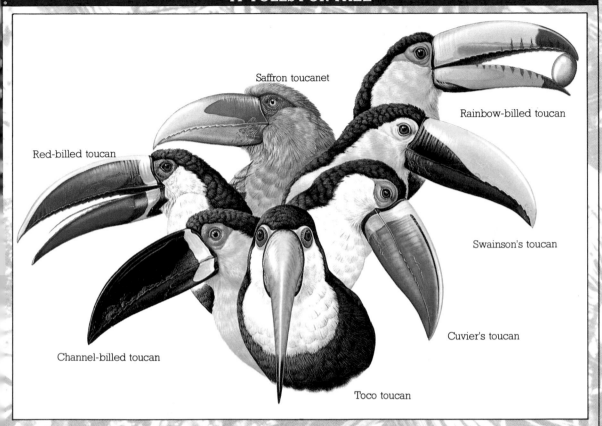

Saffron toucanet

Rainbow-billed toucan

Red-billed toucan

Swainson's toucan

Cuvier's toucan

Channel-billed toucan

Toco toucan

Fruit and berry eating toucans are among the most colourful birds found in South American forests.

Some 200 million people live in or around the forests, feeding on their fruit, nuts, honey, fish and other animals, and using their wood for fires and for shelter. In fact, most forest-dwelling tribes are wholly dependent upon their surroundings for their survival. The fact that the forests provide their livelihood is the key, of course, to the survival of these forest people. Over the past centuries they have learnt how to live only on the products from the forest. If they are destroyed – by roads, develop-ment projects, indiscriminate logging and so on – the livelihood of their inhabitants is destroyed.

Climatic stability is believed to stem from the existence of these vast forests. It is thought that forests generate considerable local rainfall, as they 'breathe' moisture into the atmosphere; without these forests rainfall declines in the area. Even rainfall patterns at the global level could be drastically altered; deforestation may also affect our climate by increasing the level of atmospheric carbon dioxide. Yet the existence of the forests is far from stable. At a conservative estimate over 1 per cent of the remaining forests are destroyed each year – or 11 million hectares annually.

Statistics like this take no account of the forests which, though they are not actually destroyed, are impoverished, with a shocking effect on plant species and on the animal and human inhabitants.

A WWF project worker has reported that the

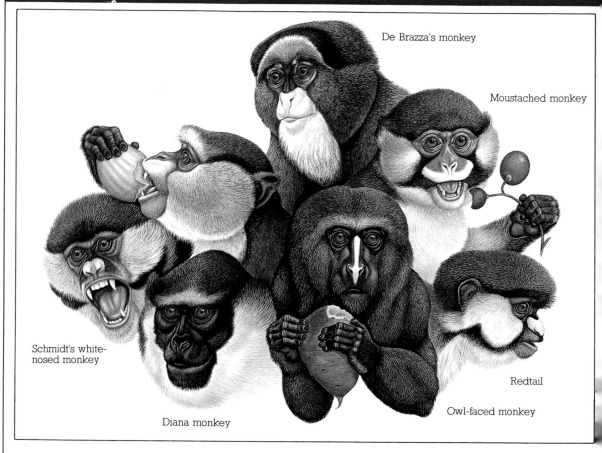

De Brazza's monkey

Moustached monkey

Schmidt's white-
nosed monkey

Redtail

Diana monkey

Owl-faced monkey

A few of the many kinds of monkeys found in the jungle.

African Violet (*Saintpaulia ionantha*) is threatened with extinction in the wilds of Tanzania where he is working in the eastern region of the country to save the forests and their plant life. The trees there are being cut down for firewood and timber, and although nearly a quarter of the estimated 2000 plant species of Tanzania exist nowhere else in the world (including the African violet) these may disappear too if the forests disappear. Exports of the African violet are estimated to be worth $30 million at retail, and WWF are making strenuous representations to the government to stop the destruction of the forests by developing alternative means of sustaining the economy of the area. Wardens are being provided to stop illegal wood cutting, and use of economic stoves developed by the intermediate technology movement is being encouraged to save trees.

To return to the urgent need to stop this forest destruction, it is important to understand the term 'wild genetic resources with potential economic value' which is used to describe those plant and animal species that have useful characteristics which can be harnassed for human beings. The aim of conservation must be to save these wild 'gene banks'. Just one example is the wild rice *Oryza nivara* which by cross-breeding has passed on its resistance to grassy stunt disease in commercial rice. This single sample of wild rice from central India is the only known source of resistance to this serious disease. Once, in the 1970's, this swept the rice-growing areas of the East, destroying more than 100,000 hectares. By using *Oryza nivara* a variety was bred, resistant not only to grassy stunt but also to other pests and diseases. Known as IR36, it is now the most widely-grown variety of rice in the world, covering some 10 million hectares. No other source of resistance to grassy stunt has yet been discovered.

How can we preserve plants? One obvious answer is to carry them off from the tropics to one of the 600 or so botanic gardens around the world. Indeed the movement to conserve plants began in these botanic gardens, where the staff were alarmed at how little was being done to save essential species. More and more, experts at places such as Kew and Missouri now see plant conservation as a principal reason for the existence of botanic gardens. Conserving genetic resources and finding better ways to make use of wild plants is the vital contribution botanic gardens are now making to international development, particularly in the Third World. In their greenhouses they maintain and propagate endangered species, store seeds for reintroduction, and provide information on the economic and medical use of plants. It is well known that it was not in the rubber forests of the East that the rubber industry was born – but in the Palm House at Kew. That kind of work continues today, perhaps less well known, perhaps on a less significant scale, but important none the less.

One of the concerned experts, Grenville Lucas of the Royal Botanic Gardens, Kew, says:

'The top priority is to protect plant habitats rather than to grow the plants in our botanic gardens. In any such garden, however splendid its facilities, plants under constant attention are still vulnerable to mechanical breakdown of the facilities – or even human error. More serious – it is rarely possible for us to maintain more than a very small proportion of any plant's genetic diversity in cultivation. So plants propagated by seeds tend to adapt rapidly for conditions in the garden rather than those in the wild.'

The woolly indri is one of many threatened primates found on the island of Madagascar.

So where are the priority areas? Tropical rain forests are rich in animal and plant species and are found in three main tropical forest regions: Africa (including Madagascar), Asia and the Pacific, and Central and South America. Within this vast area, the priorities are:

Africa: The south-western part of the Ivory Coast, lowland forests of the Cameroon, mountain forest in Tanzania, and moist forest in Madagascar.

Asia: Indonesia, Thailand and Malaysia.

Latin America: Coastal forests in Brazil, the lowland forest in Peru, the Amazon provinces in Ecuador, the Atlantic slopes of Central America.

Viable populations of primates can only survive if forests are maintained. The most threatened species in Africa include the mountain gorilla in Rwanda, Zaire and Uganda; the pygmy chimpanzee

Prince Philip visits a lemur centre in Madagascar in 1985.

in Zaire; the chimpanzee and red colobus, the mandrill and the drill in Cameroon; and the little aye-aye (described by Douglas Adams, p. 28), the indri and the sifakas in Madagascar (described by Dervla Murphy, p. 29).

In Asia the most threatened species include the orang-utan in Indonesia and Malaysia; the lion-tailed macaque in southern India; the proboscis monkey in Borneo; and the snub-nosed monkey in China.

Finally, in South and Central America, there are fears for the survival of the woolly spider monkeys and lion tamarins in the Brazilian Atlantic forests; the white uakari, southern-bearded saki and pied tamarin in the Amazonian areas of Brazil; the cotton-headed tamarin in northern Colombia; and the yellow-tailed woolly monkey in northern Peru.

It is a veritable attendance list in the Ark, and the state of these primates which depend on the tropical forests for their survival are an excellent indicator of the state of health of their habitat.

Conservationists, in protecting the forests, do not forget the mangroves – those coastal woodlands, or tidal forests which are found in tropical and subtropical sheltered coastlines, where they act as barriers against erosion. The picture opposite shows vividly the watery nature of the mangrove (and its destruction). These often form very extensive and productive forests, given suitable conditions for growth. In time, mangroves become an economic resource, acting as nurseries for young fish, and as sources for wood, fibre and other materials; they have been used in this way by coastal peoples for thousands of years. Once again, though, it is man who threatens the destruction of an ecosystem which supports man. This happens,

The small mangrove island (inset) and (above) the dreadful devastation which occurs when the mangroves are destroyed.

for example, when we change the intertidal environment by converting mangroves to agriculture and fish-pond culture, or cut them for timber.

In South East Asia and Africa, man diverts water which dramatically disturbs the mangroves by diminishing fresh water inflows. In Central America, communities such as that of Monterrico, Guatamala, are dependent on wood from the mangroves to make charcoal to boil water for salt production. WWF funds are being used to train these people to use alternative methods of producing salt, thus preserving the trees in the mangrove and the ecosystem of which it is part.

In the developed world, the coastal zone is also the scene of intense activity: we happily build marinas, ports and industrial zones, and even 'canal type' housing developments in what were once very significant areas of mangroves. It may be that we extend the quality of life in one sense, but only by destroying it in another. This is because our 'developments' eliminate the protection provided by the mangroves against tropical storms. When mangrove forests are cut, the habitat for many forms of wildlife, especially birds, is eliminated – so too the renewable timber, fuel and food resources, they will not begin to rejuvenate for many years even if their desecration is halted now.

The Hon. William Waldegrave MP on the Role of Voluntary Conservation Groups

How do things begin to get done? How does awareness of a problem first arise? At what stage does it become a matter of public debate? I suggest that World Wildlife Fund's first 25 years would not be a bad starting place for a study of how conservation issues have entered the mainstream of political thinking. For many are certainly there today. Without doubt such a study would show the critical importance of a very few, deeply committed individuals, who organise ordinary citizens into those bodies which we now call NGOs (non-Governmental organisations) or pressure groups.

But lobbying and skilful media use will only help to produce actual solutions if they are backed up, on the part of the NGOs, by proper analysis and solid research. It is all too easy to argue that 'they' should do something; that there should be stricter laws, more regulations and taxes, stronger enforcement, more action. It is much more difficult to organise and manage research to help find solutions, and ways of applying them. The success, and strength, of World Wildlife Fund is that it has demonstrated how these two approaches – pressure and direct action – can be combined to reinforce each other. In consequence, when views on and proposals for changes in public policy are pressed on Ministers and Governments, they carry greater weight.

I suspect that all Governments take an ambivalent view of NGOs. Of their very nature, active NGOs seek change in attitudes, policies and priorities. There is undoubtedly inertia in the system – and it often does appear that any pressure on Government for changes tends to provoke a corresponding pressure to resist change. If the NGO is regarded as an advocate for the prosecution, then there will be advocates for the defence – and Governments have to assume the role of judge. On the not infrequent occasions when there are sound and persuasive arguments on both sides, the position of judge can be uncomfortable.

The wise reconciliation of differing interests is never easy. Yet in the field of conservation, my own perception is that if one steps back from the day-to-day issues to consider the broad trend of developments in recent years, the major differences between Governments and NGOs concern issues of timing and practice. Not 'whether' but 'how' and

Snipe Dales, one of the 296 UK areas supported by WWF.

'when'. This surely is a great achievement for bodies such as World Wildlife Fund.

It is right that there should be a degree of tension. The relationship between Government and NGOs must never by cosy, but it must be based upon mutual understanding and respect. In Britain the Government provides very considerable funds to help strengthen NGOs in a variety of aspects of their work. Our traditions allow us to do this without any loss of independence on the part of the NGOs.

In its first 25 years, World Wildlife Fund has shown how it is possible to be a crusading body whilst achieving a reputation for objectivity, realism and responsibility. Its participation in the major international conservation conventions is welcomed by and valuable to Governments. In the UK, World Wildlife Fund and Government have worked together. A fine example is our major scheme to pursuade companies of the benefits to them as well as to the natural world of business sponsorship for conservation.

Of course there are disagreements from time to time. Differences on those many things about which reasonable people can reasonably differ. But one thing is certain, World Wildlife Fund will continue to grow in stature and both to present Governments with awkward problems to be resolved and help with their resolution.

CHAPTER FIVE

The Art of Persuasion

Unfortunately *economic development* has more popular support, particularly in countries with growing populations, than does *conservation*. Therefore it is vitally important . . . to make it clear that it is possible to reconcile the demands for development with the need for conservation *at no great cost.*
HRH the Duke of Edinburgh

The Hunter, the Poacher, the Developer – these are often painted as the villains of the piece when stories about endangered species or ravaged environments come to be written. Indeed, in the early days of WWF, the projects which were supported with funds were almost all directly related to preventing animals and plants being destroyed, and sometimes these were of a modest nature. For example:
- field equipment, such as a motor boat, for the warden of a rhinoceros reserve;
- nest boxes for endangered forest parrots in Puerto Rico;
- photographic and other equipment for a survey of flora on the Falkland Islands.

At the same time, there was already a realisation within WWF that the root causes of many environmental problems lay far from the individual transgressor and that, to achieve solutions, it would be necessary to bring pressure to bear on governments, either directly or through international agencies. The following are early examples of this:
- grants to coordinate advisory bodies on oil pollution of the sea;
- support for international projects to study migratory routes for waterfowl, so that action

Sir Samuel Baker (pictured here with his wife) published a book in 1867 which was full of information about hunting elephants, buffaloes, rhinoceros and lions. He carried ten guns on his hunting expeditions and started the fashion for big game hunting in Africa.

could be taken to protect and conserve those routes;
- surveys of national parks in South East Asia.

Before long these national and international projects were absorbing an increasing part of WWF effort. There were a number of reasons for this. Perhaps the overriding factor was the belief that governments *ought* to be playing a leading part in those conservation activities which lay within their control. As the World Conservation Strategy put it, 'Governments . . . should take the necessary steps – including changes in legislation – to ensure that conservation policies are implemented.'

It was clear to WWF that services and information should be made available to governments in order to influence their policies. WWF came to realise that appeals to the enlightened self-interest of people and governments was the way ahead – and here was an opportunity for WWF to provide leadership. It believed that it could substantially strengthen the kind of laws which governments passed to protect the environment, and also that important improvements could be made in the administration of conservation not only within national boundaries but

Conservation of tropical forests helps local people like this Wai Wai Indian in the Amazon.

between one nation and another, through international agencies.

Over $2 million has been used to fund studies aimed at improvements in conservation programmes at governmental level. One important project is the establishment of the IUCN Environmental Law Centre. In this case, WWF funding has been strengthened by additional support from governments themselves, from the World Health Organisation, the European Community, and other bodies. One result has been an agreement by the ASEAN Group (some major Third World nations) on the Conservation of Nature and National Resources, which is the first attempt to evolve a legal, binding agreement between nation states concerning the major elements of the World Conservation Strategy.

This Strategy, launched world-wide in 1980, is a kind of manifesto, not in itself having any legal authority, which was subsequently endorsed by the General Assembly of the United Nations. It is not often that prime ministers, heads of state, leading statesmen and heads of international aid organisations all speak out in favour of something, as they usually find it easier to disagree, but this is what happened when the World Conservation Strategy was launched. The name World Conservation Strategy (WCS) is a little off-putting but it was simply a document which set out the guidelines for integrating conservation with development. That sounds straightforward, yet it required a complex study of the subject by WWF and IUCN before words could be put together which would be acceptable to the thirty-eight nations which had agreed to endorse it, and to develop their own national strategies in its support. A 'national strategy' is another name for a plan of work to be done. One other aim of WCS was to select those areas and those nations whose work plans were top priority.

The countries chosen for priority attention were Senegal, Jordan, Nepal, Sri Lanka, Indonesia, Honduras, Belize and Greece. Zambia was also to be approached. Clearly, if these countries were going to agree to the plan, then WCS had to be translated into their languages, and this included an Arabic translation for Jordan and Senegal.

*Countries Preparing
National Conservation Strategies*

The general principles, which world leaders accepted, has been ardently supported by WWF over the past six years. It has concentrated its promotional efforts in the small number of (mainly) Third World countries which are the priority areas. Each year it has selected one of the main thrusts of the Strategy for special attention: in 1982/3 Tropical Forests, in 1983/4 Plants and in 1985/6 Waterlands/ Wetlands. All these efforts by WWF were executed in close collaboration with IUCN. Of course any effort to have the manifesto put into binding form (such as by the ASEAN nations) would be a great step forward.

The Environmental Law Centre uses such resources as the European Community Data Bank for Environmental Law, which is also supported by WWF. Another project involves an effort to promote a World Charter for Nature, which was adopted by the United Nations General Assembly, which means that it has the support of 111 nation states.

Related projects aim at producing a comprehensive index of all the world's species which are the subject of some kind of legislation. This enables IUCN to have up-to-date information on the kinds of protective legislation which individual governments pass to save their flora and fauna from destruction.

Another data centre supported by WWF is the IUCN and UNEP Conservation Monitoring Centre in Cambridge, England. (see also Chapter 6). Here details of thousands of individual animal and plant species are kept, which show their geographical range and status. The data is used by governments and industry to avoid, for example, conflict between development projects and key wildlife sites in many parts of the world.

An example of the data kept at the Centre is the information they store about two isolated volcanic islands. One is named after Robinson Crusoe and the other after Alexander Selkirk (the original sailor on whom Defoe's novel was based). Both are centres of Chile's seal-hunting industry. Dampier, who visited the islands in 1683, said, 'There are

The late Prime Minister Indira Gandhi greets Prince Philip on his tour of Indian conservation areas.

DEFORESTATION IS CAUSED BY:

Fuelwood Collecting   Logging and Land   Overgrazing
Clearance

DEFORESTATION HAS DEVASTATING EFFECTS:

1. Forested Hillside   2. Deforestation   3. Soil Erosion

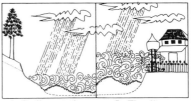

4. Sedimentation   5. Flooding

always thousands, I might say millions of them.' Indeed, his guess was probably correct for in the 18th century over three million seal-skins were shipped to Canton alone in one period of seven years. By 1880 the seals appeared to be extinct.

However, in 1965 a Chilean expedition observed 200 of these fur seals on Alexander Selkirk Island. WWF was called in to help make recommendations for the species' conservation, and a proposal has been made to establish a small reserve, manned by game wardens, on Alexander Selkirk. The seal, now protected by law, seems to be making a slow recovery. On page 46 WWF researcher Daniel Torres is seen with a fur seal pup.

A whale is an easy animal to research. They can be tracked (from their sounds), without difficulty, identified, approached and observed under water.

Sperm whales and day-old calf in the Indian Ocean.

Below: Humpback whale's fluke, Alaska.

'He roams the seas
in freedom with no
enemies save man.'

Whale research ship Tulip.

Daniel Torres with fur seal pup on the Juan Fernandez Islands, Chile.

The sperm whales move slowly in cohesive groups, but this unfortunately makes them a prime target for the whaling industry.

In 1979, after pressure from WWF and other organisations, the International Whaling Commission declared most of the Indian Ocean a sanctuary for whales. A WWF-sponsored team used such devices as acoustic sensing, snorkelers, video recording and depth sounders to establish the habits of the whale within the sanctuary area, and their results were extensively publicised. During the research, the team also heard the songs of the humpback whale, and it is believed that there is a population of humpbacks also in this area.

The humpback whale in the Atlantic was hunted almost to extinction in the 18th and 19th centuries, and it was not until 1935 that it was given international protection. Despite this its numbers are still thought to be only a few hundred.

Off the west coast of Greenland, local people are allowed to hunt a quota of ten whales a year, but WWF monitoring studies indicate that even this small offtake may jeopardise the future of the humpback in this area. Individual whales can be photographed and identified, just as human beings can be spotted from photographs – from the study of scars and other markings, as well as callosities. Whales even have 'birth marks' on back and head, and about one third of them have unique white belly patterns, which are frequently visible during courtship activities. A research vessel, backed by WWF funds, has been studying the habits of the humpback in the Greenland region, and in 1982 the population was estimated at 212 animals.

Another aspect of the study of whales is the way they are used as tourist attractions, and for other purposes, as part of a 'Whales Alive' programme. However, severe problems continue to beset the whale as exploititive whaling interests remain very powerful.

CHAPTER SIX

Threatened Like the Dodo

The fate of the dodo on Mauritius is well known. It had become flightless and so could not escape attacks on it by the seamen who visited the island in the 17th century. Today only the head and foot of one bird remains – in a museum at Oxford, dead as a dodo, as the expression has it. This will also be the fate of other bird species which cannot adapt as man destroys their habitat and pollutes the areas where they eat, breed and rest. One of WWF's priorities is to investigate the decline in numbers, and try to establish reasons for it, so that preventative action can be taken.

It may seem strange now, but twenty-five years ago when WWF was founded, there were no lists of birds and animals whose species or habitat was threatened. Certainly there was a great deal of knowledge of the problem by individual scientists and by conservationists, but there was no comprehensive data, and there was no one to set priorities. Today, the position is very different. In Cambridge, England, is one of the world's great centres of knowledge, and one of its least-known but most vital storehouses of information is the IUCN and UNEP Conservation Monitoring Centre.

This information is vital, not simply because it is an ethical principle to save species from extinction, but because the preservation of genetic diversity is both a matter of insurance and a matter of investment – necessary if we are to sustain and improve agriculture, forestry and fisheries production, and keep open new options for the future, acting as a buffer against harmful environmental change, and providing the raw (genetic) material for much scientific and industrial innovation.

The Cambridge Centre is there to monitor and record, and, most important, to make the data available to as many appropriate users as possible. But the question must be asked, 'Are we winning or losing?' The answer is that we are winning some and losing some, but, overall, it is the expert view that our planet is losing across the board, and in many cases we still do not know whether the outcome will be favourable or not. Even if we are not experts, we can each draw our own conclusions by scanning the many and varied project reports in the following pages. At the same time, it is important to remember that significant progress is sometimes achieved more discreetly and is not recorded in the various individual WWF project reports. One example of this – and a 'winning' one – is the continued success of international efforts to save the polar bear. Five Arctic nations support this by a transnational agreement (Canada, Denmark, Norway, USSR and USA).

Here, though, in a little more detail, is a selection, from the many thousands, of a few individual

Dodo, painted by John Savery, c. 1650, exhibited, with remains of a head and foot, at University Museum, Oxford. This flightless bird inhabited Mauritius but became extinct c. 1680.

All over the world butterflies are threatened by collection, pesticides and habitat loss.

projects, winners and losers which have been supported by WWF over the years.

Invertebrates, Butterflies and Moths

The butterfly population in South Korea is diminishing rapidly due to pesticides, habitat destruction, and over-zealous collecting of the 251 species known; 18 rare, beautiful or curious species are the subject of special protection.

Reptiles

Crocodiles are threatened throughout the Philippine Islands. Several kinds are in danger of immediate extinction. Protection measures, particularly the protection of their habitats, are being urgently taken.

In Mexico, the East Pacific green turtle is severely endangered through smugglers who can sell a live female in Mexico City for £1 or £2. It is estimated that more than 3000 males have perished in the feeding grounds over an eighteen-month period. Aircraft and motor boats have been used to monitor the adult breeding season. Males declined by 67 per cent in five years. WWF studies have convinced the Mexican Department of Fisheries that they must declare a total ban on the capture of these turtles.

Birds

In Siberia, cooperation between US and USSR scientists is helping to save the endangered Siberian crane. It is threatened because of hunting and by the disappearance of wetlands on the crane's wintering grounds. To ensure their survival, a captive flock of ten birds was established in Wisconsin, USA, and eventually it is hoped to restock the crane back into Asia, using the common crane as a foster parent. This is no easy matter as the Siberian crane is one of the most aggressive of birds when in captivity, and so artificial insemination became imperative. To simulate the long Arctic night, artificial lights were suspended above the enclosures where the breeding cranes were kept. Cranes usually lay two eggs per pair each year, but generally rear only one chick. By removing the eggs as they are laid, however, captive birds have been induced to produce multiple clutches.

Falconry parties from the Middle East visit Pakistan to hunt the migrating houbara bustard in the arid tracts of the Thar and Cholistan Deserts, and the plateaux. It is traditional for the falcons to be used for hunting in this part of the Indian subcontinent, and over a hundred years ago Lord Curzon noted that there was hardly a local chieftan who did not have a bird of prey attached to his wrist. Today hunting is even more intense as far as the bustard is concerned: between 1956 and 1975 it suffered a 75 per cent decline in density, and some three thousand bustards are killed each year. WWF is working with other organisations and the Government to establish sanctuaries in Pakistan and to start a captive breeding programme in Bahrein.

Mammals

Altogether there are probably 12,000 rhinos remaining in Africa and 2000 in Asia; poaching for horns is an active business. Rhino horn is often shaped into drinking cups, as there is an ancient superstition that the horn detects poison. There is also an unfounded belief that the horn and skin are

effective as medicine: the horn is powdered and drunk to cure skin ulcers, and rhino pills are made up and promoted as cures for fever, as painkillers, and to promote good circulation. None of these remedies works. Perhaps this is the reason for the encouraging news that there has been a significant drop in demand from consumers in Asia. Hong Kong and Japan have ceased to import it altogether, and sell substitutes. One of these is antelope horn, which is cheaper than rhino, and it is also more difficult to fake. However, in other areas, notably North Yemen, demand for rhino horn remains high.

China and Singapore also trade extensively in it. Africa has two races of white rhino, the northern subspecies and the southern. The northern one was only discovered in 1900. Meanwhile, the only previously-known southern race was virtually

Dr Perran Ross worked on behalf of WWF with the Oman Government to conserve marine turtles. The hawksbill turtle (below) is threatened by demand for its shell.

David Shepherd Painting the Elephants in Zambia

The BBC decided, a few years ago, to film my story, *The Man Who Loves Giants*. They obviously wanted to include an elephant sequence and they said: 'How about filming you walking up to some elephants and painting them?'

'Don't be so stupid – no one has ever been crazy enough to do that.'

'Well, you're probably mad enough, so let's have a try.' It was that marvellous British 'stiff upper lip' spirit – we'll probably all get killed but won't it be exciting?

We all trailed off to the Luangwa Valley in Zambia; myself, my wife, the programme director, the programme secretary, cameraman, assistant cameraman, sound recordist and three African game scouts. Most important, however, Johnny and Rolf also joined us. Johnny was Head Game Warden at that time and Rolf was a professional hunter.

We all piled into a couple of Landrovers and off we went into the bush. I was in the back of the second Landrover with everything ready – telescopic legs of the easel already stretched out, all my colours squeezed out around the edge of the palette and brushes at the ready. Coming round a corner, we saw an elephant about a mile away under a tree, sleepily flapping its ears to keep itself cool in the heat of the midday sun. Quietly we stopped the Landrover, and Rolf, who was driving, leaned out of the cab and whispered: 'Will that one do?'

'I suppose so.' (I couldn't even see it without my glasses!)

We stopped both vehicles and hid them in the bushes; then a quick run-down of procedures as if in a military exercise – what to do in an emergency, and how to behave. We walked as quietly as ghosts. I was carrying my easel above my head. If I hadn't the legs would have got caught up in the bushes and the elephant would have heard the jangle of the brushes and bottles knocking each other. The next thing I remember was Rolf suddenly yelling to me: 'Leave your easel and run!'

It all happened so quickly. I seem to remember three or four tons of extremely angry cow elephant suddenly running towards me. I dropped my palette, turned round, nealy knocked my wife over, and we all started belting back to the Landrovers as fast as we could. I looked over my shoulder and saw the elephant charging flat-out for Rolf, straight past my easel.

Game wardens all react in different ways in situations like this. Some

50

fire in the air. This is almost guaranteed to stop a charging elephant (so I am told!). Rolf does not believe in doing that – both of us hated the sound of rifle shots, particularly in a National Park. Rolf believes in shouting. He is gifted with a very fine deep bass voice. However, it was not the resonance of his voice echoing throughout the bush that stopped the elephant in her tracks, it was the obscenity of his language! I am totally convinced that that cow elephant spoke perfect English. I swear to this day that I saw her stop in astonishment and blink her eyes in disgust at the torrent of abuse thrown at her. It worked, but only temporarily, because after she had recovered from the shock she charged again. She charged four times at Rolf. Every time she stopped it gave us more time to get back to the Landrovers. Eventually she gave up!

For me, the elephant is the most gentle and benevolent creature of all. We know so little about him. He is highly intelligent – probably more so than most of us. I hope in a way that we never solve many of the mysteries about elephant behaviour. There is a mystical quality about elephants and I would prefer to leave it like that. Of one thing I am completely certain, having lived with elephants for thirty years in the wild in Africa: they deserve a better fate than would appear to be theirs at the moment. It is not the fault of the poor old jumbo that he carries on his head a valuable commodity. Far too many people who ought to know better will go to any lengths to deprive the elephant of his ivory using the most appalling methods – poisoning water holes with battery acid, blowing their feet off with land mines, poisoned arrows, high powered automatic weapons – there seems no limit to man's depravity. Surely this noble animal deserves a better fate.

A scientist in Wisconsin carefully packs the eggs of the Siberian white crane in a crate for despatch to the USSR to be placed in nests of the wild common crane. Fewer than 1000 Siberian cranes remain in the wild.

In the Central Kalahari Reserve is the second largest wildebeeste population in the world – second only to Serengeti. Yet it is under threat. This is because the local livestock owners are resentful about the damage the wildebeestes do to fencing and grazing facilities in the area. Research teams have already noticed that there are virtually no young wildebeestes in the herds – an ominous sign of a serious decline. WWF is funding a study of the migratory movements of these great antelope herds, so that conservation plans can be developed and presented to the Botswana Government, for incorporation in its land-planning and zoning.

extinct, down to only ten animals. Now the situation is reversed; the white rhino in the northern range is on the verge of extinction while conservation of the southern race has raised their numbers from 10 to 3000. The white rhino is a placid creature, grazing open grassland and blissfully unaware of what is happening downwind, and is thus an easy prey to man.

The white rhino was also a prey to other disturbances – the civil war in the Sudan eliminated many; in Uganda, large numbers were killed in Amin's time and in the subsequent war; they have also been lost from

Right: Falconry parties like this one from the Middle East visit Pakistan to hunt the bustard.

This picture from Lord Wolverton's book Five Months in Somaliland *has the caption: 'coming suddenly on the rhino, I fired at his heart knocking him over on the spot'.*

Chad. Then a new wave of poaching swept over Africa, particularly in the Sudan and Zaire, as the realisation grew that rhino horn could be sold for large sums. It is priced at more than $500 a kilo on the international market.

As a result, today, only about 12,000 rhinos remain in the whole of Africa. WWF has financed anti-poaching operations in Zambia and Tanzania. It has helped establish anti-poaching units in Kenya.

In Malawi, the spread of agriculture and logging has resulted in a shrinking of the elephants' habitat, and numbers are on the decline because of poaching, mainly for tusks. Poachers now hunt with shotguns, as permits and shells are easy to obtain, and there are many wounded young elephants, roaming at large in the forests. Another hunting method is to use boards with long nails which are hidden on the elephant trails under cover of grass.

ELEPHANTS (Malawi)	
Area	*Estimated Numbers**
Kasungu National Park	1,000
Nkhotakota Game Reserve	300
Vwaza Marsh Game Reserve	300
Liwonde National Park	200
Majete Game Reserve	30
Nyika National Park	low tens
Mangochi area	low tens
Ntchisi forest	low tens
Dedza mountains	few
Total	1,900

* *These figures are now probably even worse*

Right: A happier rhino being tranquillised and marked in the Kruger National Park in South Africa, watched by Prince Bernhard.

Poverty and a growing population have resulted in an increase in poaching over recent years, as the people's economic circumstances get worse, and the price offered for ivory rockets. The solution will be partly a political one: WWF must persuade governments to control the ivory trade, to upgrade law enforcement, and reduce human and animal conflict.

It is strange but true that not enough is yet known about the diet of the elephant; indeed a study of plants they eat in Central Africa recently unearthed two new plant species unknown to man – or at any rate to the scientists at Kew. The subject is an important one, because elephants tend to migrate to specific areas of vegetation, and that is where the poachers are able to find them easily, and set their traps. Poisoned lances and guns then finish off the quarry. One WWF-supported programme is aimed at a full study of elephant habits, nutrition, etc., so as to be able to establish new protected areas for the diminishing herds.

The golden lion tamarin is one of the most endangered monkeys in the world, and is now found only in a few isolated forest patches in the lowland forest of the state of Rio de Janeiro. As few as two hundred survive. A long-term ecological study is necessary to determine diet and habitat requirements so that a scheme can be devised to reintroduce the tamarin into the wild. Fortunately, captive tamarin, in zoos around the world, breed very successfully so there are good prospects for saving this attractive monkey.

Another South American monkey, the Peruvian yellow-tailed woolly monkey, was until recently thought to be extinct. Then, about ten years ago, an expedition found some in the cloud forests of the Andes. Here again, WWF has encouraged local people to appreciate the value to them of protecting this monkey in preserves.

Fish

Fishing fleets from many countries are now sweeping clean the seas round the Falkland Islands, with devastating consequences for mammal and bird species dependent on the fish resource. Chronic starvation may result for the penguins and

International efforts to save the polar bear have been successful.

other creatures. Urgent studies have been put in train by WWF to examine beached animals so as to ascertain the effect of this uncontrolled fishing, and to protect the fish themselves.

Another valuable resource of fish is to be found in the various tributaries of the Amazon. WWF has funded a $100,000-plus research project in this area to try to discover the facts about the fish collectives in about 15 Amazonian tributaries, with the aim of determining the fish migration between the various rivers – via the main trunk – so as to take steps to achieve maximum protection. One specific threat to the fish in this area is outlined in the next chapter.

Brian Clark Observes the Monarchs of the Snow

For a moment I could not grasp why the silence was so eerie. Then I realised; I was standing, as I had often stood, on a pebble beach with mountains surrounding a bay; but there was no sound of the sea. It was still. Frozen. The pressure ridges made a brave attempt to imitate waves, but the silence gave the lie to the imitation.

The first animals I saw were not the bears, but seals, dozens of ring seals, hauled out from their holes on to the ice, enjoying the sun. They were sleeping, taking 'seal naps' of from five to thirty seconds only. They, too, were on the look-out for polar bears, so they could slip back into their holes into the sea, before they became a bear's dinner.

The polar bear is one of the world's great carnivores, living almost entirely on seal. In the high Arctic there is no vegetation to speak of. The tiny alpine plants, purple saxifrage, yellow poppy, alpine ground willow, whilst they make glorious small breaks of colour on the grey moraine, provide no sort of food to sustain the 1200 lb of adult bear. It is the blubber of the seal that provides the bear with the fuel to keep up his body temperature. His life is spent in quest of his quarry.

I saw a bear on my first day. There he was loping over the ice in a steady trot, pausing now and again to lift his black nose into the air. I saw his body stiffen as he scented a group of seals three hundred yards away. His body became lower, as he stalked towards them. For ten minutes he moved slowly, but the seals spotted him and they slipped into the water. The bear moved to the hole to assure himself they were quite gone, then set off again on his loping trot to find another group.

The bear has been strictly controlled and it seems that so far this has ensured the stability of the population. The native peoples of northern Canada, the Eskimo – now properly called the Inuit – are allocated a number of bears per settlement. The village councils have accepted the need for this and the quotas are not exceeded. If the settlement wants to, it can sell the right to hunt a number of its allocation and the money raised from the sport hunters is used for community purposes.

I find it difficult to understand why anyone would *want* to kill a polar bear for fun. Need I can understand – I am not a vegetarian – but I cannot understand the pleasure of killing for its own sake. But still, some people evidently do enjoy watching a noble animal fall, its blood staining the pristine snow. If it has to happen, then it is right that it be controlled so that the species is not endangered and that the money raised be used for the benefit of a people which has always seen the polar bear as part of its total economy.

The bear roams miles; one tagged bear has be recaptured a thousand miles from its birthplace. It keeps up a steady lope over the thousands of square miles of polar ice. Its hunting technique is one of two kinds. It either stalks or 'still hunts'. In the first it uses the methods of any stalking animal, flattening itself, moving only when its prey is looking away. It is an excellent swimmer, and some hunts have been recorded where the bear has slipped into the water to surface at the edge of the ice between the seal and its escape route. On the ice the seal is no match for the polar bear and with a quick bite or two at its neck it is dead.

The still-hunting technique requires enormous patience. The bear will wait for hours beside a seal's breathing hole in the ice; as it surfaces, with one blow from the bear's paw it is dashed against the ice, and the long claws quickly hurl it out of the water. The reality of bears is a long way from childhood sentimentality. But the cult of the bear has even deeper roots in our subconscious than our childhood memories of cuddly toys. He is always appearing in one form or another in folk tales, and myths that stretch back further than man's ability to write. Because he hibernated in the winter and reappeared in the spring, he became a symbol for death and resurrection and scholars have traced the bear cult back to the dimmest beginnings of man's groping for understanding of himself in the world.

In the twentieth century the search for truth is scientific. The Polar Bear Research Unit at Radstock Bay, Devon Island, consists of a wooden hut and two tents on a 600-foot tower of rock, 200 yards across with a flat top, safe from the bears. The two scientists of the Canadian Wildlife Service kept a 24-hour watch on any bears around us, recording painstakingly every movement, how many kills they made and so on. It is important work. The Service, having studied polar-bear behaviour for over ten years, is in an excellent position to advise its own and other governments about how to conserve the animals.

And the bear. I admired his relentless tenacity, moving hundreds of miles over the ice, always looking for food, waiting for hours at a hole for a seal to appear, or, in the depths of the polar winter, burying himself in a snow den until the weather gets better. He is an exemplar of our essential loneliness. No world could be bleaker than his, no life less social, but he takes what is and lives with it.

CHAPTER SEVEN

Upsetting the Balance

A region called Serra dos Carajos, a hilly complex in the Amazon tributary Rio Tapajos, is now considered to possess the richest concentration of mineral deposits in the world. One of these minerals is gold. And the gold-miners, in their anxiety to let no grain excape them, are upsetting an ecosystem. What, it may be asked, is an ecosystem? It is not too easy to explain. The word means the total natural process. Put in mathematical terms, you could say plants + animals + place = ecosystem. An ecosystem is at its most natural when it is undisturbed by man. WWF funds conservation work in all the world's threatened

Fuel-oil pipeline crossing a freshwater reedswamp, UK.

ecosystems – including tropical forests, wetlands, dry grasslands and the sea.

To return to the gold-miners (and there are some fifty thousand of them), they have upset the ecosystem because they have destroyed the streams in their section of the Amazon by dredging and diverting water courses in the search for precious ore. Hundreds of streams are being polluted and dangerous amounts of mercury, which is used in mining operations, are being fed into the water and possibly entering food chains, with disastrous results. The fish in the polluted streams and humans who eat them inevitably suffer.

This is a simple example of the effect on an ecosystem of the depradations of man. Another good example is in Central Turkey, where a vast wetland area, the home of 134 species of bird, is being used by the local population for reed-cutting and grazing. It is also proposed to drain an area and extend a canal into the bird reserve. Some success in preserving this Turkish ecosystem has been achieved by banning hunting throughout the year in the wetlands and the surrounding area. Reed burning is also prohibited.

Where does WWF come in? It has adopted the criteria of the World Conservation Strategy that 'unique ecosystems should be protected as a matter

Reef area of Pulau Ajoc, Irian Jaya, Indonesia, where the government is a supporter of conservation measures.

of priority'. As a result it supports studies directed at protecting ecosystems from destruction. One obvious form of destruction is from oil pollution, and WWF has financed a study of the impact of oil pollution on the living resources of aquatic environments. This has become a practical hand-book for other conservation organisations. WWF has also financed a global report on mangrove ecosystems.

Another hazard to ecosystems comes from chemicals, especially pesticides. To increase yields – almost at all costs – pesticides are an apparent instant success in terms of crop improvement and in dealing with disease-bearing insects. At the same time, pesticides release toxic substances to harmless plants and animal life. Of course, certain pesticides used properly are not hazardous. But others can be, and any pesticide can be used incorrectly. For example, spraying off-season crops in irrigation schemes and flood plains may affect many more than the target species alone. Fish and birds are particularly vulnerable. Some examples of the problems are given in the table overleaf. WWF is very alert to these problems and continuously monitors world trends in pesticide use.

Perhaps one of the most interesting of the world's ecosystems is to be found in the Galapagos Islands, made famous by Charles Darwin. For more than twenty years,, the Research Station named after him

SOME EXAMPLES OF ENVIRONMENTAL HAZARDS OF PESTICIDES

Insecticides in general	vector control, foliage sprays	mortality and population change in non-target arthropods and vertebrates; development of resistance
DDT	general use	disturbed reproduction in certain species of birds and fish
Endrin	wet rice	fish mortality
Endosulfan	vector control	fish mortality
Aldrin, dieldrin	seed-dressing	mortality in seed-eating animals; secondary poisoning and population decline in birds of prey
Herbicides in general	general use	mortality and population change in non-target plants and invertebrates; secondary effects on host plant dependent arthropods
Fungicides in general	general use	disturbance of composition of soil microflora
Methyl-mercury compounds	seed-dressing	mortality in seed-eating animals; secondary poisoning and population decline in birds of prey
Rodenticides in general	various baits	mortality in non-target mammals and birds (including secondary poisoning with some rodenticides)

has promoted work to save these islands six hundred miles from the coast of Ecuador. With WWF support, the aim has been to reduce direct human impact on the ecosystem and the life it supports. Giant tortoise populations have increased, but the dark-rumped petrel is at risk (in 1985 sixty wild cats had to be killed to stop them being wiped out completely). Little is yet known about the threat to rare species like penguins and cormorants. There are new threats, such as increasingly large colonies of settlers from the mainland, with their dogs, rats and pigs. Much still remains to be done, with a need for increased funds to man the Darwin station in this, one of the last major wild habitats of plant and animal life left in the world. (See also Tom Stoppard's article on pp. 68–69.)

Right: The Galapagos Islands very much as Darwin would have seen them 150 years ago.

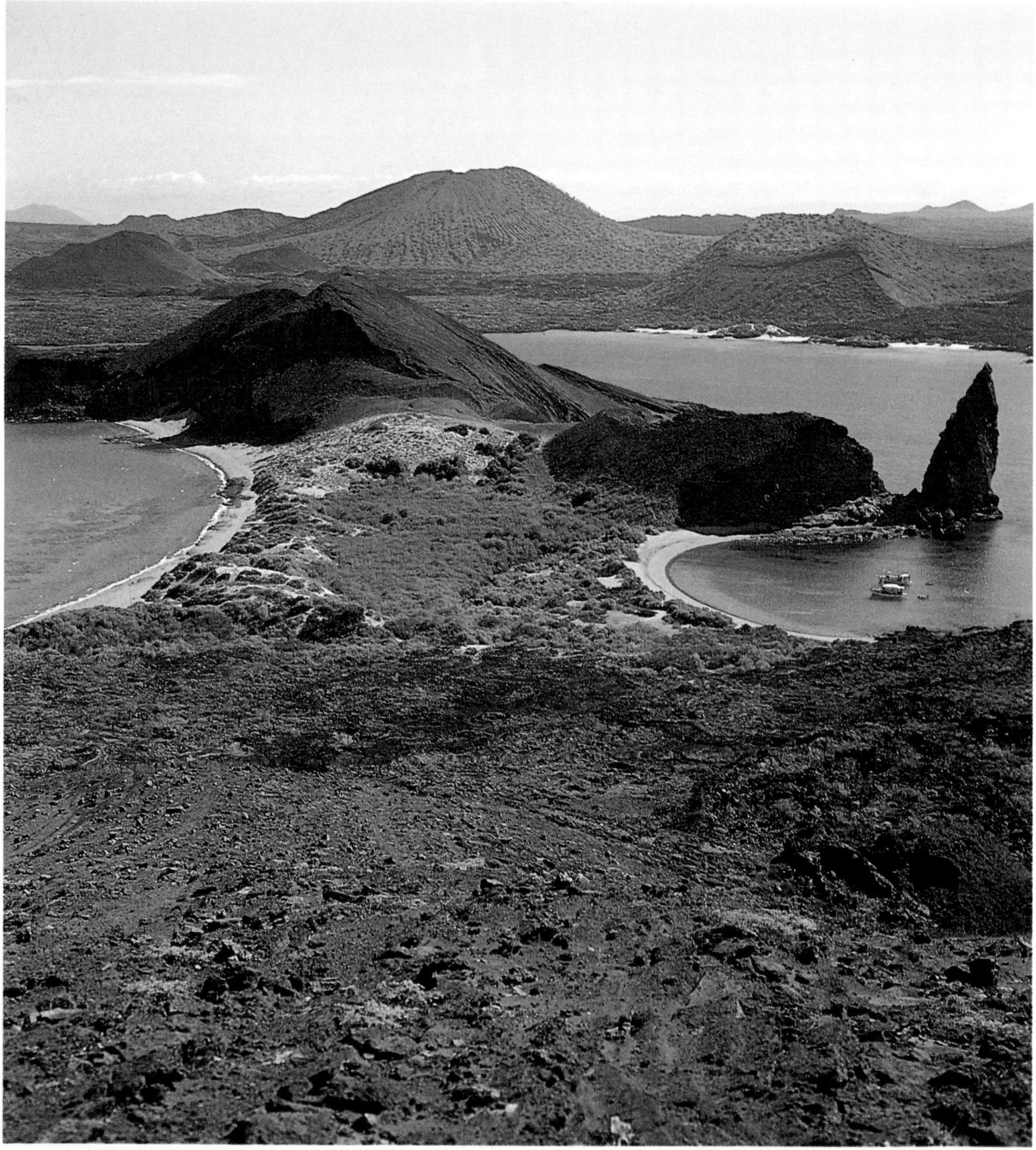

Left: A dozing Galapagos sea lion. Above: The Darwin finches whose different shaped bills stimulated the great naturalist's theories on the evolution of species. Top right: The frigate bird with its spectacularly inflated pouch. Right: Land iguana.

Left: Plants strikingly lit by a low sun on the island of Santa Cruz, Galapagos. Above: Galapagos giant tortoises gather in a pool. Right: Measuring tortoises helps with plans to ensure their survival.

Tom Stoppard in the Galapagos

The main islands of the Galapagos are twice-named, as though in accordance with a dual personality, and indeed there can be few places where paradise and purgatory are in such collusion.

We stood one morning on the broken cliffs of southernmost Española, known to Darwin as Hood and indiscriminately so called to this day by the descendants of those Ecuadoreans who claimed the archipelago, without disputants, 150 years ago. The surf destroyed itself thunderously against a shambles of black lava, washing over sunset-coloured crabs and leaving mists of spray over blowholes where the sea forced a booming passage through the rocks. Marine iguanas from the bestiary of Hieronymus Bosch, baleful little dragons with sagging throats and jaws like mean old men, waited out the millenium while gulls and dive-bombing boobies whistled a neurotic high register into the groaning, hawking din of a colony of sea-lions, whose other appeal to the senses was the stench of rotten fish.

On Isla San Salvador, called James for a Stuart king, we burnt our soles on a black petrified lake that once flowed hugely around two ochre cones of clinker, molehills as big as the Ritz. The surface of this lake was not smooth but disturbed on two scales, being broken up into tilted slabs, each slab preserving the forms of an ancient viscosity, waved, plaited and combed like women's hair. On this waterless joke against landscape a cactus hardly bigger than a shaving brush seemed as miraculous as the Palm House at Kew.

What, then, puts one in mind of paradise? Simply this, and nothing in countryside or garden, safari park or rain forest, prepares one for it: the animals are in a state of innocence. They have no idea that you and I are, as the biologists put it, the most successful of the species, and that we could choose to wipe them out if we did not choose to cherish them; and so they are not afraid.

This is more strange than words can make it. One walks among iguanas, herons, doves, mocking-birds and finches as Adam and Eve in medieval paintings walk among antelopes and cranes.

The sea-lion lies down with the snorkler. Boobies nest on the trail.

The swallow-tailed gull (the prettiest gull in the world, it has large, perfectly round, luminous black eyes set in a bright red ring, and looks as if it comes from Hamley's) and the Galapagos dove (the prettiest dove in the world, it has a plump rosy breast, blue button-eyes and speckled wings, and looks, as it has sometimes found to its cost, good enough to eat) pose for photographs.

What is Eden for the poetically minded is sheer heaven for the research biologist. It's nature on a platter. How about a study of the flightless cormorant, which dives like a seal to catch its food? Simple – get in the water with it. The flightless cormorant doesn't mind a bit.

There is that; and there is the fact that the flightless cormorant, like the Galapagos penguin, the Galapagos dove, the iguanas (land and marine), the swallow-tailed gull, the 4 kinds of mocking-bird, the 13 kinds of finch and a dozen other birds and reptiles, not to mention those giant tortoises and 228 species of plant, exists nowhere else.

Charles Darwin spent five weeks here, one week under canvas on James Island. He had set sail from a world which orthodox scholarship had ascertained to have been created at nine o'clock in the morning on Sunday 23 October, 4004 BC. Whatever Darwin made of this calculation, he had no reason to doubt that all species of being had been created simultaneously and immutably by God. The Galapagos pages of his narrative of the *Beagle's* voyage give the reader a spooky view of the penny dropping. . .

The natural history of these islands is eminently curious and well deserves attention. Most of the organic productions are aboriginal creations, found nowhere else; there is even a difference between the inhabitants of the different islands. . . Considering the small size of these islands we feel the more astonished at the number of their aboriginal beings and their confined range. . . Both in space and time, we seem to be brought somewhat near to that great fact – that mystery of mysteries – the first appearance of new beings on this earth. . .

One consequence of Darwin is that nowadays among the species to be found in the Galapagos not the least numerous is man, two of the principal sub-species being scientists and tourists.

The original 14 species of giant tortoise are down to 11, and will be 10 when Lonesome George, the sole survivor of the Pinta Island tortoise, finally pegs out. George was discovered in 1971, a mournful exemplar of the law of the survival of the fittest. The rats and dogs had thrived on the eggs and the hatchings, and the goats on the vegetation. The 10 remaining species are probably safe now.

CHAPTER EIGHT

Plants and Green Glue*

Entire plant communities, like entire species of some animals, are in danger of extinction, and in some ways the threat to plants could be more serious for man than the threat to animals – although much more difficult to dramatise. Ironically, it is man that is responsible directly for the extinction of most of this plant-life. As Peter Raven, Director of Missouri, one of the world's greatest botanical gardens, puts it:

'The worldwide deterioration of natural habitats, a deterioration that is taking place as a direct consequence of human activities, is likely to cause the extinction of what conservatively has been estimated as a sixth of the species of plants, animals and microorganisms in the world. Most of this extinction will take place in the tropics. For plants, the loss could amount to some 40,000 species well before the middle of the next century – the greatest loss of plant species that has ever occurred during a short period of time. What ought to frighten us now is that a major portion of this extinction is likely to occur during the lives, and even during the active professional careers, of those who are reading these words. The estimate suggests

*Green glue is an expression used to describe all species of plants which in themselves do not have any potential economic value, i.e. they do not contain a valuable chemical compound and they are not palatable by cattle. It is the fact that they are not palatable that makes them valuable as green glue. They are often spiny, poisonous or extensively hairy or unpalatable. They cover the ground like a crop and have a massive root system which helps to fix moving soil, tap subterranean water, and by their very nature 'stick' the ground down where it is. Green glue might be used to stop the desert moving if we can introduce other crops between it on a permanent basis.

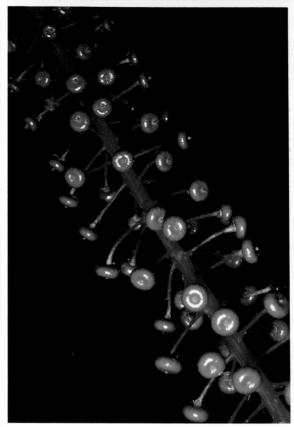

Phytolacca rivinoides *of the poleweed family, used by the Tirió to treat lice.*

the loss of at least two plant species per day over the next half century, with a lower rate in the immediate future and a much higher one in a decade or two. Only a redoubled effort to study, name, and understand the plants of the world will provide a sound basis for improving the situation, and for saving as many as possible of these plants while this is still possible.'

The first thing to be done – as well as to study the problem – is to bring it to the attention of the public. Most people think of plants as purely decorative, although there are many in the Third World who believe they have magic properties. In a way, the important functions that plants perform *can* be described as magical. They protect land from becoming desert, they influence the weather, they provide the medical products which cure even the most serious illnesses, and they are essential features of the habitat for wildlife, not to mention humans.

Now while the plants bred for agriculture, forestry or agricultural purposes have all derived from wild stocks in the past, it is vital to conserve their wild relatives now. This will ensure a source of genetic material in order to develop new strains which will adapt better to, for example, cold or arid climates, or which are resistant to disease or which may produce heavier crops or be easier to harvest.

So it is in our own interests to make certain that these wild stocks remain. Continual in-breeding of conventional developed stocks, as in the human species, is not productive of the best results. Although some species are propagated by plant-breeding centres or in botanic gardens, these are comparatively few, because the greater part of our agriculture is based on only about 30 of the estimated 250,000 species of flowering plants, of

Mark Plotkin, *working for WWF, and Indian guide collecting medicinal plants near the Surinam–Brazil border.*

which one in ten is either rare or now under threat. So there are vast numbers of plants which have not yet been studied to establish if they have a value to society. It is, of course, not only individual plants that must be propagated, but communities of plants must be preserved, just as herds of animals must be conserved in their habitats, or man in his villages and cities.

WWF, recognising the need to publicise and study the threat to wild plants, which it knew had been neglected, decided to mark the year 1984/85 by a special Plants Campaign. It aimed to raise about $4 million to fund this international effort, and national campaigns were also launched with great success. Sweden, for example, received an anonymous donation of $1.4 million for plant conservation. The campaign was launched by Prince Philip at Kew in May 1984. About 80 per cent of the funds raised were to be spent on field projects, including the Tropical Forest Programme.

Amongst these projects was one to preserve a 60-

Cephaelia, *relative of commercial ipecac, which is used for medicinal purposes in north-east Amazon.*

Catharanthus roseus, *rosy periwinkle.*

For example, the rosy periwinkle is the source of the anti-tumour alkaloids, which have achieved success in treating leukaemia and Hodgkin's disease – yet this plant was first investigated because of its use by local people in the Caribbean. Other potentially useful plants have been identified to treat cancer, to provide contraception and to enable local drug industries to be developed. This last point may be significant for many Third World economies which cannot afford to spend millions of dollars on imported drugs, particularly when they may grow the genetic stock on which those drugs are based within their own borders.

Let us turn away from medicine. Only a minute proportion of the world's available plants have ever been widely utilised for food. Only about 150 species (out of several thousand edible plants) have been developed to the point where they are traded

The hairy potato of Bolivia entraps aphids or warns them off chemically, and would be of use to man.

acre islet off the coast of Mauritius to become a readily accessible showpiece of Mauritian flora and WWF recruited wardens to prevent illegal wood-cutting. Another was in South America, where Amerindian tribes are often the only people who know the special properties of plant species. Loss of this knowledge would be a major handicap to the progress of the human race. The people of Surinam say *'Na boesi, ingi sabe ala sani',* which means 'In the jungle, the Indian knows everything'. So far, by talking to the Indians, information has been collected on over one thousand useful South American plants. It may be thought that with a massive drug and pharmaceutical industry in the West, man no longer needs to depend on plants for medicine. This is not, however, the case. Almost half of all the prescriptions dispensed in the USA contain substances of natural origin, and over 50 per cent of these in turn contain a plant-derived principal ingredient.

Wild African violets are threatened in Tanzania but millions are propagated in cultivation.

commercially. Today, fewer than 20 plant species provide 90 per cent of our food, so one could say that a mere 20 plant species stand between us and starvation. That would only be true if we failed to develop the heritage which nature has left us. Much of our current diet is based on the exploitation of tropical countries when these were under European domination. But under the colonial system, only a few species were chosen for export (Sir Walter Raleigh's potato springs to mind), so the concentration of commercial effort and research priorities continued to focus on these key plants to the exclusion of others. Even after the colonies achieved independence, the same food habits continued because the markets had been established by the colonial developers, and it is difficult to change market tastes, or create new ones, although it can be done.

Already WWF studies have identified products which local people use, but have not so far been exported. For example:

Uvilla: a small tree native to the western Amazon which takes three years to fruit, but yields a prolific harvest which can last over three months. The fruit can be eaten raw or made into wine.

Cocona: a delicious fruit grown in Peru, Colombia

and Brazil. It can either be eaten raw or made into a thirst-quenching drink.

Hwan Hwan: another fruit highly-prized in the north-west Amazon.

Palms: two varieties throughout the Amazon produce an oil identical to olive oil.

So much for medicine and foods. Another potential import substitute is for fossil fuels. There are several Amazonian plants which could be substituted for fuel, and which, since they thrive in tropical forests, would encourage man to protect the latter instead of cutting them down for pasture and eventual wasteland. These plants include the babassu palm, described as 'a living oil factory'.

Similar to coconut oil, it can be refined into edible oil, or used for plastics, detergents, soap and margarine. It contains 27 per cent protein and is an excellent fertiliser and animal feed. A single tree can produce up to a ton of nuts a year, 72 per cent of which is oil.

There are other oil and fibre plants, which are second only to food plants in terms of their usefulness to man. The Amazonian Indian uses plant fibre for housing, clothing, hammocks, nets, baskets, brooms and fishing lines. Any number of Amazonian trees could be exploited for the fibres they produce. Unfortunately the only export of any consequence for which they are at present used is Panama hats (from the *Carludovica palmato*). Some of these same trees provide, too, an adequate supply of edible oils. For thousands of years they have supported the diet of local tribes. They contain vitamins and minerals, and some could be substituted for olive oil which is currently imported.

If the conservation of endangered animals seems a massive task, how much greater is the preservation of plant life on our planet. Clearly WWF cannot do it all alone. One way of getting the most out of its expenditure is for WWF to cooperate with other agencies, particularly international agencies, and to try to influence the direction in which these agencies use their own funds. Such bodies as the World Health Organisation in Geneva, FAO (the Food and Agricultural Organisation) in Rome the International Board for Plant Genetic Resources (IBPGR) are likely targets. WWF has in fact got together with these groups to develop a coordinated programme for the conservation of economic plant species. These include medicinal plants and the wild relatives of crops in current use. All the organisations involved believe that real progress will be made towards an international cooperative programme for plant survival and conservation.

HRH the Duke of Edinburgh (here wearing the ubiquitous panama hat) visited the Sudan-Sahelian zone to promote conservation efforts and draw attention to the basic ecological problems which are aggravating the continent's on-going famine and drought. Here he visits a refugee camp where rice is being rationed.

CHAPTER NINE

Spreading the word

Sir Peter Scott, Vice-President of WWF wrote recently to the Pope suggesting that His Holiness might direct his bishops in Latin America to stop the consumption of tortoises as food during Lent. Some tortoises are threatened animals on that continent and because they are classified as fish, many Catholics regard them as a suitable food for their

A WWF education project in Madagascar helps conservation on this beautiful island.

Lenten diet, thus putting the unfortunate tortoises under still greater threat. Sir Peter's letter was perhaps unique amongst the wide variety of techniques used by WWF to put across the conservation message. Are there similar techniques which can be assured of success if – as it is – the message is desperately urgent? The answer is that the techniques of describing the problems, targets, methods, ethics and so on, involved in conservation are as varied as the message itself.

Take, for example, an Indian village. It is visited by an artist, Ranjit, who gathers the villagers round his 'pitch', unrolls a scroll of his paintings (somewhat reminiscent of a strip cartoon) and sings a ballad to the audience on the theme of conservation. As they begin to receive the message, he points out to them the painted pictures which illustrate the story of the ballad. Ranjit's visit is sponsored by WWF.

At the other extreme is *The World Conservation Strategy* thousands of which were commissioned by WWF, and was distributed not to Indian villagers, nor indeed to villagers anywhere, but to heads of

Scrolls shown to villagers warn them in pictures not to sell frogs legs to foreign gourmets as the frogs perform a vital local function by eating the insects that destroy the villagers' crops.

state world-wide, and their principal advisers. Many of the latter are involved in developing national strategies on conservation. National Committees (related to WWF) on educational projects have now been established in Argentina, Australia, Canada, China, Costa Rica, Czechoslovakia, Hungary, Ireland, Mexico, Nepal, Oman and Poland, with those in Brazil, Malaysia and Pakistan in process of formation.

The work of these committees includes encouraging teacher-training institutes to introduce environmental education into their curricula, and starting environmental field-study centres in youth camps, youth clubs, nurseries, etc. To make these efforts successful, the groups prepare audio-visual aids, organise exhibits, prepare teacher back-up material and so on. An example of a specific project in this context, was the decision to bring the birds back to Mount Subasio in Italy where St Francis once lived and preached. In the centuries since the little birds were made famous by St Francis, the depridations of hunters and gourmets had depleted the bird population in this most respected of sanctuaries. Now Mount Subasio has become a protected area, where the killing of birds is prohibited, and there will be an educational centre at the site. The site itself may not be large, but its educational significance is of course immense.

Much of this work is, naturally, projected at the young. It was in 1975 that WWF/IUCN set up its first

Mobile Unit for Wildlife Clubs of Uganda, designed and constructed by WWF/IUCN International Education Project.

practical conservation programmes for young people. Now it has programmes in over fifty countries, and has produced nearly a hundred audio-visual programmes to support local and national conservation activities as well as global campaigns.

In 1976 WWF equipped two mobile units based on the Renault F4 which were sent to the Gambia and Senegal in West Africa to tour schools, colleges and villages giving exhibitions, talks and audio-visual presentations. Each van is fitted with a portable generator, 16 mm film projector, slide unit, public-address system and display screens. The visits to these areas were so successful that similar units were sent to Wildlife Club centres or similar associations in Cameroon and Uganda, Zambia, Sri Lanka, Madagascar and Rwanda. Fiji, Ethiopia and other countries have also been visited. These mobile units have proved most effective when working in close contact with existing organisations' Wildlife Clubs, for instance, rather than on their own. A visit is followed up by the despatch of visual-aid material such as posters.

It has already been noted that the techniques of promotion vary. For example, in Indonesia the emphasis has been on self-help. Project staff were sent there to help set up a dark room, build up a slide library and produce 'in-house' a technical book on Indonesian wildlife.

Another successful technique is based on the 'teach the teachers' principle. WWF assisted in the

setting up of a centre in Gloucestershire, where trainees from Africa, Kenya, Malaysia and other countries have completed ten-week courses on 'Communication Conservation'. The aim is to provide teachers with a thorough working knowledge of environmental principles and to teach them the practical skills needed for effective education in their own countries. This includes such basic know-how as the essentials of photographic techniques and offset printing.

Reference has already been made to the

Left: College students in Tanzania study the behaviour of a live elephant. Below: In Zambia, both elephants and rhinos are at risk from poachers. WWF has been supporting the national Chongololo Clubs which spread environmental awareness and appreciation amongst the young people of the country. There is a parallel radio club with its own weekly thirty-minute radio programme. This realistic elephant was built by Zambian children as an exhibit at an agriculture show. The message: IT'S AN OFFENCE TO SHOOT WILDLIFE.

slaughter of birds in Italy. Indeed the Mediterranean region is notorious for the wholesale extermination of migrating birds. One necessity, if attitudes to bird life are to change, is education, to bring about greater knowledge of bird life in the region; it is a remarkable thing that several Mediterranean countries have no simple bird books of any description. WWF decided to rectify this, and, together with the European Committee for the Prevention of Mass Destruction of Migratory Birds, they produced such a book, specifically for Mediterranean readers. The book is given a national identity, each country having its own title, cover and text. It is hoped that if the public become more aware of the variety of birds and their natural history, they will combat the annual indiscriminate killing of millions of song birds and birds of prey for sport.

Some WWF projects are even more specific. For example, in the early 1980s, local studies in Mali, Mauretania and Senegal by a Canadian scholar revealed that a major problem for villagers was the shortage of firewood and the immense time (and therefore cost) of collecting it. This was not, of course, a new problem. Mungo Park in his book of travels, published nearly two hundred years ago, describes meeting desert-dwellers who were engaged in the arduous search for firewood. But perhaps it was a surprise to find the same problem today – aggravated by the continuous increase in population in the region, and the destruction of forests. An urgent study is now under way to try to find alternative sources of fuel to help overcome the problem.

To return to projects which are rather general in their scope, WWF has contributed to the cost of educating young people in conservation issues by the establishment of *Amis de la Nature* clubs in Cameroon schools. The clubs may be general, but their studies are sometimes very specific: a recent one was an investigation into the causes of bush fires, particularly the practice of burning off vegetation for agriculture and big-game hunting.

Another general project has been mounted in the East Caribbean where for over 300 years, development has been linked to agricultural

The ceremonial planting of a tree in Kenya brings home to all the onlookers the need for action as well as education.

production – tied to the land, not the sea. There is no marine tradition and the sea is believed to be a threat, not a resource. Yet the Caribbean is an island area in which the potential harvests of the sea are being eroded by mis-management by local people – already stocks of conch and spiny lobster have been virtually wiped out.

WWF has funded a major educational programme to try to change attitudes to the sea and improve public understanding of Caribbean marine resources.

Altogether, WWF spends annually some $500,000 on training and education, but perhaps this figure alone does not do justice to the overall educational nature of all WWF activities, which it would be difficult to quantify.

Margaret Drabble Reports on the Struggle to Save Elephant and Rhino from the Poacher

Most of what I knew about ivory poaching before setting off to Zambia was gleaned from Conrad's *Heart of Darkness* and an article in the *National Geographic* magazine. I hadn't expected to meet Mr Kurtz or his modern equivalent, but neither had I expected that within four hours of my arrival I would be stumbling over a hoard of tons of confiscated ivory that bore a startling resemblance to the hoard described by Conrad himself eighty years ago.

The only differences were that this remarkable pile was not in a hut but in a strong room at the Department for Lands and Natural Resources in Lusaka, and that I was being shown it by Mr Zyambo, the Director, and Mr Mwenya, the Chief Warden, who were emphatic that it was not fossil, but poached. Huge tusks of varying quality, some painted white, some decorated with elementary carvings (an effort, I was told, to redefine their status as trophies in a court of law, if caught) were piled high to the roof. And not only tusks: there were several trunks full of equally valuable rhino horn that had been returned from Frankfurt airport on its illegal way to the international market.

It was an awesome sight, a vivid demonstration of the scale of the problem that afflicts Zambia and other African countries.

Luangwa is a kind of Paradise. It is the second largest national park in Zambia, with one of the richest stocks of game in the world. Here is God's plenty, and those who stay at Mfuwe Lodge can't miss it for a moment.

In the lagoon below the terrace wall hippo snort and wallow and rise up, crazily decked in Nile lettuce. Goliath heron and sacred ibises stand and survey the water: a fish eagle swoops as you drink your evening beer. An elephant browses on the far bank. Vervet monkeys sit on doorsteps waiting for a biscuit.

And it is, of course threatened; which is why I was there. Ivory and rhino-horn poaching is a major problem, and people talk about it with endless fascination. Rhinos are an endangered species, and to protect them the Save the Rhino

Trust was set up in 1979, initiated by the Wildlife Conservation Society of Zambia, and backed by the World Wildlife Fund and the Government. President Kaunda himself is well known as a wildlife enthusiast, and it's hoped that his active support will combat the apathy (and even corruption) that is suspected in some quarters.

Luangwa also contains, I was told, the largest continuous population of elephant in the world; this too is threatened. Ten years ago the price of ivory rocketed, and some people estimate that the number of elephants has been halved. It doesn't, to the uninformed observer, look as though the elephant is in immediate danger: on the contrary, there are stretches where it looks as though it is on the verge of eating all other species out of house and home. One can travel through miles of landscape that look like the aftermath of the First World War, covered in stunted trees, stripped, broken, trampled. Some even argue that a cull will be necessary, but conservationists believe that it's essential to eradicate poaching first and to allow the area to stabilise: only then will it be possible to estimate the carrying capacity of the territory.

The Zambians must learn to look after their own game, I was told. This way of putting it makes one of the more disquieting aspects of the whole enterprise immediately apparent. I was disturbed on many occasions during my visit by the suspicion that conservation is a white man's luxury occupation, and a very expensive one at that: the tourist trade associated with game (big-game hunting, photography, safaris, even bird-watching) is at the luxury end of the market. The native Zambian attitude to wildlife is very different from the European. For one thing the Zambian languages don't distinguish between various forms of wildlife: the same word, *nyama*, serves for both 'game' and 'meat', and there is not a local word for poacher – Zambians use the word 'hunter', as the concept of poaching doesn't exist.

But how can such education be imposed from without, and why should people accept it? I was assured on all sides, from the Wildlife Conservation Society to the Zambian National Tourist Board, that Zambians do now realise that it is in their own best interest to preserve their own national asset; I was assured that Zambia had learnt from the mistakes of the Kenyans, who over-commercialised their national parks and safaris; I was told that now the Rhodesian war was over (which incidentally, had in itself proved a great conserver of wildlife, frightening off poachers with land mines and guerillas) Zambia would become a top tourist country. It may be so. The hard currency of the tourist is certainly welcome: maybe it will after all save the rhino.

81

CHAPTER TEN

Towards Planet Protection

The last twelve months of WWF's first 25 years of existence was described by a leading environmentalist* as: 'a critical period for environmentalists and practitioners of development alike. The focus was Africa. Many agencies, and not a few experts, were forced to rethink their positions. Two interlocking and terrible trends dominated that great continent. Environmental bankruptcy, on a continental scale hitherto unrecorded in the history of the human family, underscored the futility of much of what has passed for "development" over the last four decades. The ecology of one sovereign state after another collapsed across the Sahel and into the Horn of Africa. The whole of sub-Saharan Africa experienced extremes of climate, ranging from increased rainfall in equatorial Africa to drought in territories to the southeast and west. And we were forced to contemplate the agony of the malnourished mother and her innocent, dying child. Both are the victims of the failure of development.

'Today, one in every 200 Africans is a refugee, either from armed conflict or from ecological breakdown. With only a tenth of the world's population, Africa has one quarter of the world's refugees. Human suffering, *in extremis*, is the daily routine for millions of her people. Despite a temporary break in the drought in Zimbabwe, Kenya and a handful of southern states, hunger drives the people of that magnificent continent to the very fringes of survival. Poverty is rampant. During the year, thirty-four nations received food

*Brian W. Walker, President, International Institute for Environment and Development.

aid – at best a temporary, inadequate and essentially undignified response to human need.

'Disasters, emergencies and catastrophes are on the increase around the world. Wherever human communities get out of step with their natural environment – imposing as a consequence intolerable strains on the biological carrying systems of nature – pain, anxiety and suffering are the inevitable human result. Political instability, and even the toppling of governments, is the social result.

'The thin mantle of green that sustains all living organisms, with its fragile water supply, its critical

Wood collection is a daily task for these African children.

The richness of a tropical reef is exposed at low tide.

oxygen ratio and its twelve inches or so of fertile soil, is under powerful, unrelenting assault across each of the five continents of our planet. In the Sahelian zone and in equatorial Africa, climate is a major feature leading to the collapse of human communities – but human folly and mismanagement act throughout the world either as a trigger to collapse, or as an accelerator that multiplies the effects of mistaken development. Acid rain in Scandinavia, the Bhopal disaster in India, the erosion of the fertile hills of Guatemala, the expanding deserts of the

entire globe all tell the same story. Human beings are stretching the nature's environment to the limit of her endurance. Once the critical threshold is passed, human life is forfeit.'

Brian Walker concluded however 'The situation is not hopeless. On the contrary, the forces of sanity and common sense are exerting an increasing and formative influence.'

This is not a Doomwatch book. No suggestion is being made that the planet faces some kind of nuclear winter if the conservationists' warnings are not heeded. There need be no universal disaster of that magnitude in the 25 years ahead. So far as the past 25 years are concerned, much that has happened is regrettable, but much of it is not irreversible. That being said, there are urgent things to be done if the next 25 years is not to be a period of drift ending in some kind of major (and irreversible) disaster in the early years of the next millenium.

The goals set by conservationists can be won. This is because the scientific knowledge, the technology, the money and the manpower exist to make them achievable. What may be lacking is the political will – or rather, political understanding.

Success or failure may almost certainly depend upon a growth of man's awareness of what has to be done – and this understanding, perception, grasp (call it what we will) is not the same thing as knowledge. It is not easily taught; indeed, it may not be possible simply to present the facts in order to change attitudes. Max Nicholson, one of the founders of WWF, puts it like this: 'We know that man's brain doubled in size some time before what we now call 'civilization' began about ten thousand years ago and now he has to take on a whole new depth of understanding with the same sized brain. Can he do it?'

One must not underestimate the strength of those forces which are driving towards destruction of the planet's resources. One of the most powerful is the growth of the world's population. Startling global figures – such as the fact that it has multiplied five times in the past 150 years – are hard to grasp. But when we hear that Kenya has an *annual* population growth of four per cent, it is not difficult to comprehend how that beautiful country could quickly become as threatened as its neighbour Ethiopia is today. There are other forces as destructive as population growth, and the questions must be asked – is the conservation movement appropriately equipped to counter them?

On any reasonable assessment, WWF has proved itself to be a major pillar of the conservation 'church' and it is a very broad church pillar at that, embracing all kinds of attitudes from the radical to the more conservative, and very far-reaching in the range of its supporters, both geographically and culturally.

It has been a movement of people rather than one which has concentrated on targets. Of course, there have been targets like 'Save this or that threatened species' but because individual people have supported WWF, it has in turn been able to find people to carry out its projects, and to cooperate (sometimes within their own organisations) in common activities. It would be true, therefore, to describe WWF in human terms, as a 'caring'

Animals like the rare Goeldi's marmoset will disappear for ever if forests continue to be destroyed.

HRH Princess Alexandra, President of WWF–UK, meets Tim Walker, Chairman of WWF–UK, and his wife, Rosemary, at the Wildscreen Film Festival in Bristol in 1984.

organisation which has not lost its humanity as it has expanded or as it has relied more heavily on changing technology of the times.

Indeed, this technology of our age may well be one of the most significant factors in what Max Nicholson calls 'turning the human race round 180 degrees'. By this he means achieving a complete change of attitude towards our environment, not through education, but through realisation of what must be done. The spread of television must have played an extraordinary part in that realisation – in 'opening people's eyes' as we say. For one thing, television is no longer local or even national. For another, it does not rely, like books, on a language;

no words are needed to bring home to the viewer the horror of an Ethiopian disaster. The word 'viewer' is significant, as it implies that the television audience is made up of eyes rather than ears. And when we consider the 'global village' created by television and video, it is clear that there is here the most powerful medium for conveying the conservationists' message.

The message is one thing; the money to make it effective is another. Emotive appeals do not necessarily raise the required amounts of money, and there is the need for research, and for data-based information on which appeals to governments or to international organisations can be founded. It has been alleged that there is only a given amount of money available for conservation and environmental projects and that a successful appeal by one organisation simply works by attracting funds which would otherwise have found their way to another. Bob Geldoff's appeal was criticised on these grounds, but WWF has never believed that the argument was based on a realistic appraisal of the facts. Its view has always been that the bucket of donations was bottomless, and could be continuously filled to meet the requirements of the movement, provided always that the facts of the case were properly understood and presented.

There was a time, too, when the richer nations of the world viewed the flora and fauna of the tropics as something to be studied in the abstract. Tourism has changed all that. A 'natural resource' may now be a 'resource' of the tourist trade, just as may a pyramid or an art gallery or a great cathedral. It may be that some people have come to regard the natural world – which conservationists want to save – as justifying its existence simply because it provides this raw material of the tourist industry.

There is no harm in the concept of the world's natural resources as a 'bank' of pleasure to the tourist, any more than it is harmful to ignore their role as an inspiration to the artists through the ages. But there may be harm in consequently looking at our planet's resources as having primarily an economic value, whether it is value to the tourist or the developer or to whomsoever. It may also be harmful to think of conservation in terms of the quantity of successful projects – the sum total of all the examples – and more – listed earlier in this book, as if so many tigers, so many pandas, so many whales and so on can be added up to produce the ultimate achievement. That is not likely to be the way in which, if our attitudes are to be changed over the next 25 years, we should see the matter. Put quite simply, and in conclusion, conservation is 'a moral obligation which our generation has towards the future'.

The original doodle which Peter Scott turned into the famous symbol.

The Queen with Sir Peter Scott, Epsom 1973.

The Four Pillars – A Summary of the Aims by Elspeth Huxley

Here is the first pillar of the World Wildlife Fund: to preserve before it is too late, as much as possible of what survives of this natural heritage, to feed the hungry in spirit and the under-nourished in mind, and to hand it all down intact.

We give money to provide playing-fields for children and seaside holidays for the old; to buy great pictures for the nation, build cathedrals, put on operas and plays. Conserving wildlife falls into the same class. All are objects of beauty which give pleasure to mankind. It is no less vandalism to destroy the works of nature, than the achievements of mankind. The sheer enjoyment of nature and wildlife by people is the second pillar.

Some may prefer the scientific argument. They might put it first. The quest for knowledge has always been a major pre-occupation of mankind. A continuing curiosity is one of the characteristics which set him apart from other animals. Studies of the wildlife of this planet are in their infancy and now there is a likelihood that some of them will never be made. If we fail much wildlife will vanish before scientists can subject it to a proper study. There are species threatened already with extinction before the facts about their life-cycle are known.

Others may prefer the equally strong economic arguments for wildlife conservation. Most of the underdeveloped countries exist mainly on subsistence agriculture. They lack industries, communications, social services; their standards of living are painfully low; richer nations have to help to support them. To develop what industries they have is an urgent and an overriding need. One of these is tourism: and it is one of the most promising.

Wild animals are an asset, an important asset, to these under-developed countries, not only as a bait for tourists but as a source of food. They can feed the hungry on the spot. Venison has always been a major source of protein in parts of Africa. Instead of dwindling, as is now the case, this source could be developed and increased by the 'cropping' of surplus animals, who often support themselves much more efficiently on poor soils and pastures, and in the face of drought, than the domestic herds and flocks with which men have been trying to replace them. Wild animals thrive where cattle and sheep die of disease or starvation, or, where they survive, trample and erode the

pastures. Wild animals do not often destroy their habitat; domestic animals, without careful management, almost always do. Buffalo convert poor pastures into protein more efficiently than cattle. Why not preserve, and then crop, the buffaloes? The hungry can't be fed for ever by the charity of others. Here is a chance to help some of them to feed themselves.

The rights of the thing; the spiritual refreshment and recreation; the pursuit of knowledge; the potential economic development; these are the four pillars on which rest our appeal for funds. Time is not on our side. And failures cannot be redeemed later. Once a species is extinct, or a wildlife retreat exploited for some other purpose, the process cannot be reversed. The animal is gone for good, the retreat permanently surrendered, and the world that much the poorer – for ever.

Man is the lord of creation, king of all he surveys. A good lord does not destroy his fellow creatures, nor a king reduce the world he surveys to a wasteland spattered with clusters of brick, steel and concrete and a network of arterial roads. It will be a sad day – sad for man – if, looking through the window, he can see nothing but reflections of his own weary, baffled and disillusioned face.

WWF-WORLD WILDLIFE FU

PACE
OUT
FOR WWF
PLANTS

Left: Botanist and broadcaster David Bellamy donning his boots for the WWF annual sponsored Walk for Wildlife. Above: Sarah Greene and a group of children at the launch of Cadbury's Wildlife Bar in Covent Garden in 1985. Above right: David Shepherd displaying his magnificent elephant painting, sold in aid of WWF. Right: Rolf Harris helps to promote WWF's Operation Tiger, April 1982. Far right: Spike Milligan clearly enjoying his involvement in WWF fund raising!

Anniversary at Assisi

The central Italian town of Assisi was designated the site to launch a campaign of events highlighting the 25th Anniversary of World Wildlife Fund. Assisi was chosen in honour of St Francis, who, already in the 13th century, was preaching nature conservation. He described all living creatures as 'his brothers and sisters'.

From the start of the anniversary, WWF pursued a three-pronged campaign aimed at increasing training in conservation skills, heightening public awareness of conservation issues, and promoting conservation education.

Modern communications, however brilliant we believe them to be, fail to reach two-thirds of people worldwide. One of the goals in the anniversary year was to reach a much greater variety of target audiences through a series of major events. The aim is to mobilise many new constituencies in support of conservation for the good of nature and mankind. All the main religions, for example, contain teachings involving a respect for nature.

During the two-day conference in Assisi, speakers from economic, scientific and religious fields present papers on the importance of conservation to their respective constituencies. Representatives from the media, education, politics, and rural communities explain how best to reach each group with an effective conservation message. In the meantime, in the spirit of true pilgrimage, walks involving people from more than 30 countries converge on Assisi from the villages of the Umbrian countryside.

Simultaneously, spiritual leaders of five major world religions – Buddhism, Christianity, Hinduism, Islam and Judaism – begin a unique two-day retreat to meditate on the conservation ethic of their respective faiths.

After the conference sessions, walkers join delegates in a conservation festival on the theme of man and nature, involving traditional theatre from around the world. The religious leaders hold an ecumenical service – the first interdenominational meeting of its kind. The retreat distills the essential message which each religion has for conservation. Through declarations made at Assisi, these are then relayed across the religious and secular world.

The suggestion for the meetings at Assisi came from WWF President, HRH Prince Philip, Duke of Edinburgh, who is particularly concerned with disseminating the conservation message as widely as possible.

'WWF's 25th Anniversary and the Assisi event are milestones in our evolution. However, we must remember that milestones are no more than markers on a journey.

WWF has reached a significant stage in its development by joining with the world's major religions in an imaginative drive to bring the crucial importance of conservation to the notice of millions of people.

We have a long way to go. Assisi and our 25th Anniversary represent an exciting and challenging stage in our journey, one which I hope will strengthen the resolve of more people to work for conservation.'

Charles de Haes, Director General, WWF International

SOME OF THE WORLD'S THREATENED ANIMALS AND PLANTS

MAMMALS
Greater Bilby (Australia)
Hawaiian Hoary Bat (Hawaii)
Tassel-eared Marmoset (Brazil)
Black Spider Monkey (French Guiana)
Volcano Rabbit (Mexico)
Short-tailed Hopping-mouse (Australia)
Wolf (N. Hemisphere)
Marine Otter (Chile)
Jaguar (Latin America)
Mediterranean Monk Seal
  (Mediterranean)
Juan Fernandez Fur Seal (Chile)
African Elephant (Africa)
Indian Wild Ass (India)
Grevy's Zebra (Somalia)
Black Rhinoceros (Africa)
Pygmy Hippopotamus (Sierra Leone)
Scimitar Horned Oryx (Niger)

REPTILES AND AMPHIBIANS
Narrow-bridged Mud Turtle (Costa
  Rica)
Mexican Spotted Wood Turtle (Mexico)
Chaco Tortoise (Argentina)
Hermann's Tortoise (Albania)
Leatherback Turtle (Ocean)
Hawksbill Turtle (tropical waters)
Spectacled Caiman (Peru)
Nile Crocodile (Africa)
Mountain Chicken (Montserrat,
  Caribbean)
Olm (Yugoslavia)

BIRDS
Jackass Penguin (Angola)
Shoebill (Rwanda)
Dwarf Olive Ibis (Sao Tome)
Sokoke Pipit (Kenya)
Pollen's Vanga (Madagascar)
Wattled Crane (Zaire)
Ethiopian Bush Crow (Ethiopia)
St Vincent Parrot (St Vincent,
  Caribbean)

California Condor (USA)
Philippines Eagle (Philippines)
Madagascar Serpent Eagle
  (Madagascar)
Noisy Scrub Bird (Australia)
Horned Guan (Guatemala)
Western Tragopan (Bhutan)
Corncrake (UK)
Merlin (UK)
White-bellied Black Woodpecker
  (Korea)

INVERTEBRATES
Black Coral (tropical waters)
Queen Conch (Bermuda)
Giant Clam (Indonesia)
Freshwater Pearl Mussel (North
  America)
Edible Snail (Europe)
South African Giant Earthworm (South
  Africa)
Red-knee Tarantula Spider (Mexico)
Giant Torrent Midge (Australia)
Queen Alexandra's Birdwing Butterfly
  (Papua New Guinea)
Large Blue Butterfly (Europe)

FISH
Humpback Chub (USA)
Pirarucu (Amazon Basin)
Short-nosed Sturgeon (North America)
Fiery Redfin (South Africa)
Cherry Barb (Sri Lanka)
Giant Catfish (Mekong Basin)
Neko Gigi (Japan)
Short-jawed Kokopu (New Zealand)
Opalescent Pearl Fish (Brazil)
Asprete (Romania)

PLANTS
Coontie Palm (USA)
Chatham Islands Forget-me-not (New
  Zealand)
Dwarf Beet (Greece)
Duck River Bladder Pod (USA)
Lundy Cabbage (UK)
Shrubbycress Rocket (Spain)
Cucumber Tree (Socotra, Yemen)
Old Father Live Forever (St Helena, UK)
Golden Gladiolus (South Africa)
Waddy-wood (Australia)
New Zealand Parrots-bill (New
  Zealand)
Yeheb Nut (Somalia)
Snow Mimosa (Brazil)
Spiral Aloe (Lesotho)
Three Kings Cabbage Tree (New
  Zealand)

This species list has been selected
from the IUCN Red Data Books

SUGGESTED FURTHER READING

Our Green and Living World – The Wisdom to Save It, Lucas, Defilipps, Ayensu, Heywood. Cambridge/Smithsonian

Green Inheritance, Anthony Huxley. Collins/Harvill

In the Rainforest, Catherine Caufield. Heinemann

Wild India, Guy Mountfort, photos by Gerald Cubitt. Collins

Travel Diaries of a Naturalist, Volumes I and II, Sir Peter Scott. Collins

David Shepherd: The Man and His Paintings, David Shepherd. David & Charles

The Wildlife Parks of Africa, Nicholas Luard. Michael Joseph

Pyramids of Life, H. Reader and J. Croze. Collins

The Living Planet, David Attenborough. Reader's Digest

The Track of the Wild Otter, Hugh Miles. Elm Trees Books

Run Rhino Run, E. & C. Bradley Martin. Chatto & Windus

Sea Guide to Whales of the World, Lyall Watson. Hutchinson

Wealth of Wild Species. Storehouse for Human Welfare, Norman Myers. Westview

Discovering the Countryside with David Bellamy, Coastal Walks. Hamlyn

Bird Behaviour, Robert Burton. Granada Publishing

Antarctica – the Last Wilderness, Stanley Johnson. Weidenfeld & Nicholson

International Wildlife Law, Simon Lyster. Grotius Publications

Cry of the Kalahari, M. & D. Owens. Collins

Macmillan Guide to Britain's Nature Reserves

Tiger! Tiger!, Arjan Singh. Jonathan Cape

World Conservation Strategy. IUCN Publication

Environmental Revolution, Max Nicholson. Pelican

IUCN Red Data Books: *Mammals; Amphibia–Reptilia*, Part I; *Plants; Invertebrates; Swallowtails; Threatened Birds of Africa*. (IUCN/ICBP). Red Data Book series available from Conservation Monitoring Centre, 219c Huntingdon Road, Cambridge, CB3 0DL

Animals have always been an inspiration to artists. This cheetah, an endangered animal, was sculpted by John Kenworthy.

Acknowledgements

Especial thanks to Max Nicholson and Guy Mountfort, both early members of the World Wildlife Fund. Also to Grenville Lucas of the Royal Botanic Gardens, Kew, and Brian Walker, President of IIED, for permission to quote their remarks and to Ian MacPhail for the information about the *Daily Mirror* World Wildlife Fund edition. Thanks also to the Hon. William Waldegrave MP, Minister of State for the Environment, Countryside and Local Government, for his piece. Finally to Ginny Lawlor and Sandra den Hertog for editorial assistance.

The contributions from Douglas Adams, Brian Clark, Margaret Drabble, Tom Stoppard and Gore Vidal were originally published in the *Observer* in fuller form and we are grateful for permission to publish these shorter versions. Elspeth Huxley's contribution was orginally published by the World Wildlife Fund, and a fuller version of the contribution by Dervla Murphy originally appeared in *Departures* magazine to whom we are grateful for permission to reproduce.

The pictures and photographs are reproduced by kind permission of the following: Peter Scott (introduction drawings), Peter Jackson (pp 21 & 22), Holland & Holland (pp 23 & 54), the Oxford University Museum (p 47), Ralph Thompson (p 52), Jonathan Kenworthy (pp 94–5), David Shepherd (p 51), Pictor International Ltd (pp 22 & 93) and Sally Anne Hughes (p 5); Richard Orr drawings (pp 4, 33, 34 & 96) taken from *Jungles*, Marshall Editions Ltd. Other illustrations come from the World Wildlife Fund picture library, both in Geneva and Godalming.

WWF addresses are: WWF International, CH-1196 Gland, Switzerland. WWF (UK), Panda House, 11–13 Ockford Road, Godalming, Surrey GU7 1QU.

Caryota

Helmeted wood duck

Orang utan

Glomeropitcairnia erectiflora

Pelagodoxa henryana

Mountain gorilla

Bird-wing

Imperial parrot

Gigasiphon macrosiphon

Black caiman

White-winged wood duck

Lycaste suaveolens

Sumatran rhino

THE BRINK OF EXTINCTION